WHAT IS LIFE?

IS VOLUME

32

OF THE

Twentieth Century Encyclopedia of Catholicism

UNDER SECTION

III

THE NATURE OF MAN

IT IS ALSO THE

13TH

VOLUME IN ORDER OF PUBLICATION

THE TWENTIETH CENTURY ENCYCLOPEDIA · OF CATHOLICISM ·

Edited by HENRI DANIEL-ROPS of the Académie Française

WHAT IS LIFE?

By RENÉ BIOT, M.D.

Translated from the French by ERIC EARNSHAW SMITH

HAWTHORN BOOKS · PUBLISHERS · *New York*

First Edition, March 1959
Second Printing, June, 1959

NIHIL OBSTAT

Joannes M. T. Barton, S.T.D., L.S.S.

   Censor Deputatus

IMPRIMATUR

E. Morrogh Bernard

   Vicarius Generalis

Westmonasterii, die XXVIII NOVEMBRIS MCMLVIII

The Library of Congress has catalogued this publication as follows:

Biot, René, 1889–
   What is life? Translated from the French by Eric Earnshaw Smith. [1st ed.] New York, Hawthorn Books [1959]

   92 p. 21 cm. (The Twentieth century encyclopedia of Catholicism, v. 32. Section 3: The nature of man)

   Translation of Poussière vivante.
   Bibliography: p. [93]

   1. Biology. 2. Man.   I. Title.   (Series: The Twentieth century encyclopedia of Catholicism, v. 32)

QH307.B513   574   59–6728

Library of Congress

CONTENTS

INTRODUCTION

"Remember, man, that dust thou art, and unto dust shalt thou return." No Christian can ever lose the memory of this sentence; on the morning of Ash Wednesday it is repeated for each one of us by the priest as he makes the sign of the cross on our foreheads, and marks us with a pinch of the greyish dust from the ashes of last year's blessed palms.

"Thou art dust." The words are indeed awe-inspiring. They confront us with the fact of death, the doom which no man can escape; nor can we fail to perceive the lesson of humility which they are intended to convey. Nevertheless, it is surely a matter for wonder that, at this peculiarly solemn moment at the beginning of Lent, a moment when the Church intends to prepare us to celebrate Christ's victory over death and summons us to deepen our spiritual lives, we should be compelled to recognize that we are nothing more than a handful of inert matter.

Long before modern chemistry had demonstrated by scientific analysis that our living flesh is composed of the same material as the earth, man had learned from direct observation that, from the moment when life ceases to animate his material body, there remains nothing to distinguish him from any other compound substance, and that by the process of decomposition he reverts rapidly to dust.

What then is this magic force which endues the clay with life?

Because Life is constantly before our eyes, and because anything we see constantly loses the power of astonishing us, we tend to grow accustomed to the miracle of the plants and the animals and of man. We become almost indifferent to the wonders of nature, and neglect to inquire into the how and the why of that force which rears an oak from an acorn, creates a bee or a bird from a single germ-cell and implants in them the instinct which guides them in their intricate manner of life; which, even more, determines the flexible structure of the youth and the plastic strength of the grown man, and provides above all a dwelling-place for the mind.

This little book aims at helping the reader to take greater account of these mysteries and of their importance and significance. It is the result of many years of reflection nourished by familiarity with the labours of the experts. We cannot, of course, be expected to be masters of all the subjects embraced in an inquiry such as this: we have throughout been compelled to learn from others. We have therefore naturally had frequent recourse to quotations, taken purposely from easily attainable books rather than from learned but not readily accessible works. With the same object of being easily understood by every reader, we have as far as possible avoided the use of strictly technical and consequently somewhat forbidding terms.

In support of our policy of borrowing from the writings of others we may quote the illustrious precedent of Pascal. "Let no one say that I have said nothing new; the arrangement of the subject is new. When we play tennis, we both play with the same ball, but one of us places it better. I had as soon it were said that I used words employed before. And in the same way if the same thoughts in a different arrangement do not form a different discourse, no more do the same words in their different arrangement form different thoughts!"[1]

Our own contribution to this book consists solely in the order in which we shall submit our successive questions to the recognized authorities. Our aim is by this means to direct the reader's reflections towards the solution of the great and dramatic problems posed by the facts of life and mind.

[1] Pascal, *Pensées*, Everyman Edition, p. 7.

CHAPTER I

DUST

THE BASIC MATERIALS

Scales in hand, the imperturbable scientist presents us with the results of his inventory: the living organism is revealed as consisting principally of water. Not only does the human body contain about five quarts of blood, but every tissue is brimming with fluid; in fact, the desiccated skeleton of a man of average height weighs only thirteen pounds.

Further analysis reveals a total of fifty kilogrammes (110 lb.) of water to twenty kilogrammes (44 lb.) of solids, the latter composed of various mineral substances. Duly weighed and measured, the champion athlete's body is finally reduced to a handful of dust.

Nor must we overlook a further fact. "After combustion, the ashes of organic substances are no longer representative of the true mineral composition of the substances. A number of elements, constituting organic molecules, remain in whole or in part in the residue of the process of combustion. This happens in the case, for example, of sulphur, phosphorus, iron and magnesium. There is nothing to differentiate them from the same elements deriving directly from mineral sources. Moreover, incineration sometimes involves a certain amount of loss."[1]

Of the resulting constituent elements the most essential are carbon, hydrogen, oxygen, nitrogen, phosphorus, sulphur,

[1] Maurice Javillier, *La Chimie des êtres vivants*, Paris, 1951.

chlorine, potassium, sodium, magnesium and iron, some of which occur far more frequently than others. Their number is relatively small in proportion to the ninety-three known elements.

If we include, says Javillier, the water contained in the tissues, "oxygen acquires exceptional importance from a quantitative point of view"; but he adds that it may be advisable to consider living matter apart from its water content, and to apply the facts to dry matter.

If we do this, we find that carbon re-asserts its supremacy, forming fifty per cent of most substances and seventy-seven per cent of some, such as fats. "The biological predominance of carbon is extremely striking. Yet carbon forms only about 2/1000ths of the earth's crust, occupying a modest eleventh place in the list of elements . . . its biological pre-eminence is constantly due not so much to the amount in which it occurs in our earth, as to its atomic structure, its reactive capacities, its fitness for forming compounds, and its diffusion in the form of carbon dioxide."

From the quantitative point of view, carbon is followed by oxygen, hydrogen and nitrogen; and these four elements alone constitute ninety, and often even more, per cent of the dry matter of many organisms.

If we care to make a close analysis of a specimen organism and to arrive at the proportion represented by the chemical elements just mentioned [phosphorus, sulphur, etc.], we observe that they constitute nearly one hundred per cent of the given substance. Owing to defects in analysis, we cannot be certain that our dozen or so elements do not reach the full one hundred per cent; but we know from other experiments that something is missing. This "something", however, amounts to only a few ten-thousandths of the whole. It follows that almost the whole of living matter is composed of no more than a dozen chemical elements. Any others that may occur are present in insignificant amounts. Nevertheless, application to carefully selected substances of the finest methods of analysis, expressly devised for the purpose, reveals a remarkable increase in the number of chemical elements present in the tissues.

The following examples are given: in one hundred grammes of dry matter we find a few milligrammes or tenths of milli-grammes of zinc and copper, together with a few thousandths or ten-thousandths of milligrammes of certain substances such as arsenic.

"Finally we observe that living matter is composed princi-pally of elements of low atomic weight, the most important ranging from hydrogen (atomic weight 1) to calcium (40) or iron (55)."

Our chemists, who are proud of a science capable of pene-trating the ultimate secrets of the universe, would add that the basic materials thus selected, weighed and classified are found to be present everywhere in our environment: no doubt the amounts vary, thereby distinguishing one thing from another, but in the last resort they retain their identity throughout the entire universe. The time may come when the physicist will carry his atom-splitting to the point where nothing remains but energy. Meanwhile the analytical chemist discovers in the living organism the same components as are found in all existing things: they form the ultimate texture of the universe.

The homely simile in which the Bible story tells us that God created man from the mud is seen to be strictly accurate. It is of earth that we are made: dust we are, and to dust we shall return.

INCREASING COMPLEXITY OF ORGANISMS

From the chemical elements bodies distinguished by analysis are built up molecular compounds of ever in-creasing complexity which constitute everything we call matter.

As we know, chemistry divides the elemental substances

into acids and bases. When an acid meets a base, either accidentally or by human agency, an inevitable reaction follows which, in the absence of other factors, is invariable: a new substance appears, more complex than its component units, to which chemistry gives the name of "a salt". This salt possesses properties of its own, differing from those of the two substances which have combined to produce it. For example, a pinch of common salt (dignified by the scientific name of sodium chloride) exhibits properties unlike those of either sodium or chlorine. Only chemical analysis is capable of rediscovering its original components. Nevertheless, the relationship between the salt and its components is undoubted, as is proved by our capacity to produce it experimentally from its constituent elements, advancing so to speak from the original substances until we arrive at a salt. Conversely we can, if we wish, break the salt down into its component substances.

Every one of these facts is now common knowledge among educated people, with the result that insufficient tribute has been paid to the labours which revealed to mankind the laws governing these phenomena. Too seldom do we remember that this science and the power which it confers are of recent date. Yet it was only in 1772 that Lavoisier, then barely thirty years old, proved that "all combustion is the result of combination with the oxygen of the air". It is as well to quote his exact words, since they constitute one of the chief glories of French science. The original text may be found in R. Massain's *Chimie et chimistes*[2] (*"Chemistry and Chemists"*), which has the advantage of providing the reader with the most famous passages from the works of the great scientists. Five years later it was Lavoisier again who, by heating mercury, succeeded in analysing air.

After the genius of Lavoisier had provided a scientific formulation of the constitution of matter, the knowledge thus acquired has led to a growing mastery over nature.

[2] Paris, *Éditions de l'École*, 1952.

Step by step man has gained an insight into the increasing complexity of the structure of matter. The progress achieved is demonstrated in a list drawn up by Stanley and Grabar. Beginning with water, molecular weight 18, we proceed to glucose (180) and di-hydrostreptomycine (731). Further up the scale the figures become so astronomical that as written they require to be multiplied by a million, a method of notation which allows the molecular weight of ovalbumin to be written as 0·040. Very soon, however, we come to viruses, either singly or in dozens: the tobacco mosaic virus, which has been given great prominence by scientists owing to its position on the borders of animate and inanimate matter, has the figure 43; and the red blood corpuscle which concludes the list, reaches 173,000,000, a figure which must be multiplied by our coefficient of a million. The brain reels at numbers such as these. Astronomy is not the only science to open a window on the infinite.

At the same time, moreover, the chemical formulae and technical names used to represent the structure of organic substances have become so increasingly elaborate as to baffle the layman, just as the terms used in pathology have become almost incomprehensible to anyone unfamiliar with the technical language of medicine. For an example we may quote the name reported recently in a daily newspaper to be used in the campaign for the extermination of rats: $\alpha\beta$-acetylethylhydroxycoramin.

Simultaneously the experts have exercised all their skill in representing in diagram form the structure of molecules, and in plotting geometrically the various interconnections between their component elements. A structural formula of this kind can often occupy a large amount of space on a page of print.

All this is admirable: such formulae have paved the way to further researches and inspired fresh discoveries. Enquiring minds were led to speculate on the possibility of transmuting elements, and finally succeeded in creating new substances hitherto unknown in nature. Many such successes were achieved in the field of endocrinology, and in the synthetic preparation of hormones which have the advantage, compared with those obtained from glandular extracts, of producing biological effects of greater specificity.

It would not be in accordance with the scope or purpose of this little book to describe in detail the endless combinations exemplified by living things. In any case, such attempts are quickly overtaken by the march of discovery. Only yesterday, for example, our attention was called by the medical journals to neuraminic acid, which has been known for only a few years, and whose functional importance in many phenomena of animal and vegetable life is becoming increasingly appreciated.

What must be insisted on, as of decisive importance at the present stage of our discussion, is the supremacy in this field of chemistry, and the absolute submission it demands to its laws.

THE CHEMISTRY OF THE VITAL FUNCTIONS

Thus we see that chemistry has advanced far beyond the analysis of the molecular structure of egg albumen: we now know, for example, what human blood consists of. This is not merely a question of analysing a few cubic centimetres of blood taken from the veins and treated as dead matter. We can now take the blood as it courses through the veins in fulfilment of its vital rôle and observe what chemical processes are taking place in it, what substances it derives from the liver or from some internal secretory gland. Here once again we may be permitted to emphasize that the two examples which come most readily to mind are both due to the fine achievements of French science. Mention of the liver reminds us that it was Claude Bernard who in September

1855 reported to the Académie des Sciences his experiments with "washed liver" which demonstrated its "glycogenic function"; while it is to Brown-Sequard, a native of Mauritius, that we owe the papers read on June 1st, 1889, to the Société de Biologie in Paris on the therapeutic properties of testicular extract.

Without entering into detail, we may note that chemistry has succeeded in grouping the organic components of living beings in a small number of categories, although in point of fact "the chemical structures occurring in life are numerous, and there is no living species or tissue which does not exhibit its own specific chemical property". As Javillier says, the classic distinction among these basic components is between the carbohydrates, the lipids (commonly called fats) and the proteins (formerly known as albuminoids).

These organic compounds are linked to the simple substances previously mentioned by a chain of superposed compounds. It is the living organism (a vital and characteristic point to which we shall return) which is both author of and actor in this chemical activity. The factors involved are joined and disjoined in turn, some building up gradually into more and more complex substances culminating in the actual tissue of the living creature, while others, on the other hand, break down the complex molecules into simpler components.

By this means it becomes possible to follow step by step what may be called "the Odyssey of a mouthful of meat" after it has been swallowed for food. We begin with a process of diastatic hydrolysis, i.e. an at least partial dissolving under the influence of a digestive fermenting-agent or enzyme (proteinases). This results in the formation of what the chemist calls amino-acids. These are subsequently "de-aminated", that is to say they lose the properties of the amines, which are a group of derivatives of ammonia (chemical formula $R-NH_2$). "Deamination" may result either from oxidation and formation of a ketonic acid, or from hydration and formation of an alcohol-acid, or from reduction and formation of an acid, or even mere ablation of one of the components (NH_2) and formation of a non-saturated acid. It is usually oxidation that occurs in animal organisms.

The second act (for Javillier, like all chemists, seems to be watching a play) consists of "decarboxylation". There is no need for us to follow step by step this breaking up process, nor to give the technical terms used to describe the various substances successively encountered as we move down the scale towards chemically simpler substances. As we all know, we arrive finally at urea, in which form the residue of the ingested protein is excreted in the urine. Urea is a substance of relatively low toxicity, despite the popular notion that its excessive accumulation in the blood, due to impaired functioning of the kidneys, is a cause of alarm to the doctor who has ordered a test for the amount of urea in his patient's blood.

In the lipids, and also in the carbohydrates, we find the same processes at work: molecular break-down followed by a temporary build-up of simpler substances, which are in turn subject to fresh decomposition.

Thus we see that, for the purposes of nourishment, the body decomposes the large molecules which are ingested as food, and which might appear to the laymen nearer in complexity to those composing the body itself. They are decomposed into substances whose chemical structure becomes progressively simpler, until finally nothing is left but still simpler substances which are excreted. This reduction of food to the simpler state enables the organism to survive.

It is no doubt this apparent contradiction that is expressed in Claude Bernard's famous saying: "Life is death". At first hearing, such a remark coming from such a man is disconcerting and appears paradoxical, as Bernard himself recognized. On reflection, however, the epigram is seen to be full of meaning. The pungent formula sums up our own observations, and deserves to be remembered.

But this saying recalls another and contradictory remark by the same author, which refers to the process of anabolism, or building up. We should, indeed, be indulging in only a partial view of reality if we confined our attention to these processes of reduction to simple components. For at the same time as the breaking down, a constant work of elaboration is going on, as a continuous process of synthesis builds up the living tissues from their constituent elements. Great emphasis is laid by biochemistry on the rôle played by carbon in metabolism. "Life on this earth," says Javillier, "depends on the capacity possessed by certain organisms to construct the first organic molecules out of water and carbon dioxide. Any who lack this capacity are driven to seek their food from organic matter already contained in the environment."

Nowadays every schoolboy is familiar with the part played by plant life in this field, due to its chlorophyl content, and with the way in which animals depend on plants for their food.

To sum up, each one of us is a kind of factory comprising a number of laboratories equipped in every detail and constantly at work. No help is required from us in these combinations of molecules, nor, at any rate so long as all goes well, are we even aware of the vast operations going on within us.

SYNTHESIS OF ORGANIC SUBSTANCES

The investigation, briefly described above, into the physico-chemical composition of living matter promised to provide a complete insight into the secret of life. Yet scientists remained unsatisfied. They had succeeded to a certain extent in taking to pieces the exceedingly complex machinery of life; but for a long time they had been forced to acknowledge their inability to manufacture the very substances whose composition they had so successfully analysed. In this respect it seemed to have reached a dead end. It looked as if only the living creature itself had the power of building up one or other of the complex substances distinguishable by analysis.

Nevertheless, science succeeded in meeting the challenge thus presented. The date was a memorable one in the history of biology and chemistry, as important as the discovery of radioactivity and the splitting of the atom which were to follow a few years later.

It was in 1828 that a German chemist, Friedrich Wöhler, synthesized urea in the laboratory. He was already famous for his discovery of the surprising fact that different substances may have the same chemical composition. The rival experiments of Liebig, working in Gay-Lussac's laboratory in Paris, and of Wöhler, working under Berzelius in Stockholm, culminated in the concept of isomerism which was to achieve world-wide renown.

In his synthesis of urea Wöhler started from potassium cyanate and ammonium sulphate. "I can manufacture urea," he exclaimed triumphantly, "without any need for kidneys or even for an animal, whether man or dog." This was indeed a conclusive discovery: a further step had been taken in the identification of the biological activity of living beings with the reactions taking place between their inert components— in other words, dust.

The year 1890 witnessed a new triumph: the synthesis of glucose, the chemical term for the sugar circulating in the blood. Glucose had featured in Claude Bernard's famous experiments concerning the function of the liver which suggested to him the conception, destined to prove so fruitful, of the "internal secretion" of certain glands.

But there was more to come. Diels, starting from carbon, succeeded in synthesizing cholesterol, a substance produced in the human body by the hepatobiliary system which is an important link in the chain of steroids. Carbon, which is extracted from the soil, was demonstrably linked to the bile produced in our viscera, and an infinite vista was thereby opened up.

As we have already observed, even the hormones, to which we must now return, have yielded first to analysis, and then to synthesis at the hands of the chemist. Although these substances, which are produced in living creatures by the endocrine glands, have proved to be infinitely complex in molecular structure, their composition is so well understood that they can now be manufactured in unlimited quantities by the chemical industry. In 1934 a German, Butenandt, succeeded in synthesizing folliculin, one of the ovarian hormones, from the beans of the soya, a leguminous plant indigenous to Japan. In the same year a Czech, Ruzicka, also using soya beans, produced testosterone, the male hormone, simply as the end product of a series of chemical reactions. In 1936 it fell to the American Kendall to synthesize one of the hormones produced by the adrenal glands.

This discovery takes us into a field where the establishment by experiment of a link between what is secreted by a living organ and what begins by being merely a piece of chemically defined matter is even more sensational than the experiments with urea or even with glucose.[3] For these hormones, whether produced spontaneously by the organism or manufactured in the laboratory, not only act on the body but play a decisive part in the balance of the whole personality. They not only produce organic and nervous symptoms but affect our mental and emotional life.

[3] What is said here applies equally to the vitamins, which also play an essential part in metabolism.

VITAL PHYSICS

While analytical chemistry is engaged in breaking down material substances in order to understand their structure, physics is conducting a parallel investigation into the vital phenomena of the organism. Its approach is different, in that it directs its attention to relations of forces and manifestations of energy, as if it were examining an engine or an electric battery.

Now we find that physics, like chemistry as we have described, discovers the same phenomena and the same laws at work in the living creature as in inorganic matter or in the machines constructed by man's inventive genius.

Thus we find that Professor Boutaric of Dijon, in his scientifically accurate and readable little book *La physique de la vie*,[4] is able to present a picture of the mechanics and of the energetics of life as if he were dealing with a system governed exclusively by the laws of physics, and using the same terms as he would apply to a machine.

"In physics," he explains, "we speak of a system as possessing energy when it is capable of doing work, and we measure the variations in energy which it undergoes in passing from one given state to another by the amount of work which it has done or undergone during its passage."

This energy may indeed take different forms. It may, for example, consist of movement, when it is called kinetic energy; or it may be held in reserve as it were, as in a coiled spring before release, when it is called potential energy; or again it may consist of the generation and liberation of heat, when it is called calorific energy, and so on.

The basic principle of physics is that in any isolated system, i.e. one that is not subject to external interference, the amount of energy remains constant. Its manifestations, however, may change, or rather interchange, since there is a

4   Paris, 1948.

strict equivalence between the various forms assumed by energy. For this reason they are always subject to the same standard unit of measurement, derived from the metric system and from our method of computing time. The unit adopted is the joule, i.e. the quantity of work required to raise one kilogramme to the height of one metre. In the case of heat the unit of measurement is the calorie, i.e. the quantity of heat required to raise the temperature of one kilogramme of water by 1 °C. This unit is conveniently called a large calorie, since it is often necessary to calculate in microcalories, which are a thousand times smaller.

The equivalence, to which we have drawn attention, between the various forms of energy is expressed in the formula adopted following Joule's famous experiments: "The disappearance of a quantity of work equivalent to 426 kilogrammetres is accompanied by the production of one large calorie; while the disappearance of a large calorie in a steamengine corresponds to the production of work amounting to 426 kilogrammetres."

Physics has demonstrated that living creatures are energy-transformers, and are subject to the same laws of equivalency as inanimate matter. It is thus possible to calculate vital energy: after analysing the chemical constituents and molecular breakdown of foodstuffs we can proceed to measure the amount of calories they provide. Science has succeeded in determining the calorimetry of an animal as easily as that of a boiler, and in defining the principles of thermodynamics: the living creature is subject to the law of conservation of energy.

Even more interesting are the phenomena of osmosis, which seem to initiate us still further into the mystery of life. In this field it is once more a Frenchman, Dutrochet, who occupies the most prominent place. By osmosis we mean the passage of water across a membrane, which may be of either animal or vegetable origin, such as a pig's bladder, which forms a kind of partition between, for example, pure water and a solution of sugar. Here we approach the work performed by the living cell, which absorbs or exudes the substances with which it is brought into contact by the circulation.

Phenomena of radiant energy also occur, such as the action of light or of Röntgen rays or radio-active substances.

The vast field thus opened up in recent years has enormously increased the diagnostic and therapeutic powers of medical science. It is difficult for us to imagine a time when radioscopy was not available: yet that time was not so very long ago.

And now with our own eyes we are witnessing the application in the biological field of artificial isotopes, by whose aid we can penetrate the inmost secret of the physico-chemical reactions conditioning the vital processes. As every schoolboy knows, the atomic weight assigned to the elements, carbon, phosphorus, iodine, etc., actually represents an average of a number of bodies possessing strictly identical chemical properties and distinguishable only by physical methods: such bodies are called isotopes. By "bombarding" with rays we obtain radioactive isotopes. By this means we possess— or more exactly we produce—radioactive iodine, radioactive phosphorus, radioactive carbon; and owing to their radio-activity we can follow their passage through the body. By these methods we have acquired a more exact knowledge of, for example, thyroid secretion; or again, thanks to radioactive phosphorus, we can measure more accurately the blood volume and circulation rate.

At the same time, moreover, another field has been explored; that of the production of electrical phenomena by the living creature, or conversely the effect produced on a given biological phenomenon by the electricity generated by industrial appliances.

So we see that the "physics of life" cover an ever widening field: and we trust that enough has been said to arouse the reader's appetite to know more, and to follow with us our excellent guide, Professor Boutaric.

THE HUMAN ENGINE

With the aid of chemistry and physics combined, we can now form a picture of the living human being which may be conveyed by the term "human engine". Indeed, to the scientist man resembles a machine, a machine whose yield can be estimated, and whose mechanism is analogous to the gears and wheels and cables assembled by the engineer to form an industrial machine.

By this means it is possible to measure the power of a man at work as one measures the power of a car's engine. The standard unit of measurement is called horse-power, abbreviated h.p., which is the power required to raise 33,000 lb. avoirdupois one foot per minute. Applying this unit to the muscular output of a man working for eight hours we arrive at approximately 1/9 h.p. In the case of an intense expenditure of effort, as in a long-distance race, the figure reaches approximately 1/2 h.p.

If we examine more closely the mechanism by means of which a man succeeds in performing "work", as the physicist uses the word, that is to say if we observe the muscular contraction, we again find chemistry involved with physics.

The muscle fibres exhibit their peculiar contractile characteristic under the influence of a stimulus which may be mechanical, such as a cut or prick; such stimuli were employed by Swammerdamm in his early experiments on the muscles of frog's legs; or the stimulus may be electrical: the names of Volta and Galvani are remembered for having supplied roots for the technical terms used in measuring electric currents. But at the same time muscle consumes chemical substances, and exhibits a peculiar sensitivity to certain substances, some of which may act as a stimulus, others as a brake, while others may have an inhibitory effect.

Still further advance has been made in the exploration of the vital mechanism by the attempt to solve the enigma of what are called nerve impulses.

In this case we are no longer concerned with what happens when a muscle contracts in response to an electrical stimulus which may be brought about at will, and whose point of application, moment of action and intensity are thereafter subject to control. What we are now investigating is what happens in the nervous system itself when it sets its machinery in motion; what goes on when it despatches more or less automatically its "motor message". Various kinds of activity are here involved. We may be dealing with the automatic contractions of the heart muscle, or with the contractile fibres of the digestive tract, which function without our conscious and voluntary intervention (fortunately, since these processes are best carried on in the silence of the viscera); or we may have intentionally activated an arm or a leg or our vocal apparatus.

We have no space here to describe the present state of knowledge concerning the action of the nervous system.

Principally as a result of Lapicque's experiments it is possible to calculate the intensity of a stimulus as a function of its duration. Consequently we are able in practice to measure and compare in different muscles the length of stimulation required to produce contraction, and thereby to understand how the muscle reacts to different stimuli, and how its reactions vary according as it is in a state of repose or of fatigue. The way is thus opened for a quantitative and therefore more exact understanding of the processes operating in a man in an average state of health.

Better still, the nerve centres themselves have become amenable to scientific investigation, and their response to stimulus can be recorded in graphic form with its variations in repose or in action, in health or disease. The knowledge thus acquired can then be applied to the diagnosis of "nervous" diseases by means of electro-encephalography.

PHYSICAL CHEMISTRY OF MENTAL ACTIVITY

The brain centres are the mind's instruments, and may therefore be considered the noblest of human prerogatives. Nevertheless, the material changes which accompany or underlie the subtlest intellectual process or the most unselfish feeling of emotion are found to be identical with the chemical reactions and physical phenomena exhibited by inorganic matter.

Suppose, for example, we begin by analysing the composition of the "neuron", which is the technical term for the nerve cell. In the protoplasm, the material basis of every kind of cell, we find present the same basic elements which we have already found in the body as a whole. Water constitutes eighty per cent of the grey matter properly so called, and sixty per cent of the nerves. There are also present proteins, lipids and carbohydrates in somewhat unusual proportions, since the nerve cell contains an exceptional amount of fat or lipids, to give them their technical name. Among these fats we distinguish sterol derivatives, substances which, like the simple fats found in all parts of the body, contain carbon, oxygen and hydrogen, but whose alcohol component is a sterol instead of glycerol. Later come lecithins, which are compounds of glycerol and phosphoric acid, followed by syryngomyelins and cerebroids. . . . We quote these technical terms merely in order to indicate both the accuracy of scientific knowledge in this field and the complexity of molecular structure; and also in order to demonstrate once more that every investigation of the material basis of thought confronts us with a substance identical with that of which organic matter is composed.

When the brain is functioning it breathes; that is to say it absorbs oxygen and eliminates carbon dioxide, as was proved by experiments carried out about 1870 by the French physiologist Paul Bert. It is this powerful respiratory action of the brain which draws the most oxygen from the arterial blood whence it derives its chemical nourishment, and it performs this function at a rate twenty times faster than does a muscle at rest. It has been calculated that 100 grammes of cerebral matter absorb from 600 to 800 cubic centimetres of oxygen a minute. Moreover, this amount can increase by more than 100 per cent under the influence of strychnine, or diminish under an anaesthetic. The absorption of oxygen by other parts of the nervous system, such as the sciatic nerve, has been calculated with the same accuracy.

Similar experiments have been carried out to ascertain the consumption by the nervous system of other chemical substances, particularly of glucose, the proteins, etc.

In the light of these facts, the reader will have already perceived how changes in the cardiac cycle, and particularly a sudden fall of pressure, can interrupt the action of the heart and bring on a fainting fit. In the same way changes in atmospheric pressures have an immediate effect on the functioning of the nervous system.

More detailed research has been carried out on the way in which the "nervous apparatus" works, and a close scrutiny has been made of the method by which this "engine" consumes chemical elements. The process has been vividly described by Chauchard:

When a nerve cell is stimulated with sufficient intensity, whether by natural or artificial means, whether by electrical, chemical or mechanical action, it produces an electric wave, the nerve impulse, which travels to the end of the nerve fibres, spreading the stimulation which may subsequently be transmitted to other contiguous cells. . . . The stimulus, by a purely physical operation consisting in reversing the electric charge, has annihilated the superficial electric charge maintained on the cell by its chemical activity in a state of rest, and which serves it as a protective shell. The cell reacts by attempting to stop the gap. Its chemical reactions are intensified, since it requires more energy to counter the discharging action of the stimulus or to recharge itself than is required when the cell is

at rest. The conflict between the stimulus which aims at discharging the cell, and the chemical activity which aims at maintaining the charge, produces a nerve impulse.

To begin with, the stimulus prevails and the charge on the
cell decreases: then the chemistry of the cell restores the
charge. The whole process is rapid, lasting not more than from
a few thousandths to a few hundredths of a second in the case
of the quick-conducting and slow-conducting nerves respec-
tively, the first phase of the process lasting only one third of
the whole. The interval between the exhaustion and the re-
plenishment of the nerve's energy is called the refractory
period, which lasts for a few thousandths or hundredths of a
second and thus determines the maximum frequency of the
impulses.

All this activity is accompanied by chemical phenomena.
"The energy required for the immediate recharging of the
nerve cell is supplied instantaneously by the decomposition
of a molecule of adeninepentosetriphosphoric acid, which
explodes, as it were, when subjected to stimulation: then,
almost at once, during the brief refractory period, this substance, of which there are no great reserves, is reconstituted,
preparatory to breaking down once more in order to produce
a new impulse." Enough has been said to demonstrate con-
clusively the material nature of what goes on during the
passage of that subtle something called a "nerve impulse",
and to convince the reader that in the last analysis the entire
process is the product of physical and chemical phenomena.

A PHYSICAL ANALOGY TO THE NERVE IMPULSE

The realization of the analogy between the process at work
in a living organism and in an inorganic machine led to the
invention by Lilie in 1918 of what has been called an "artificial nerve". This does not mean that a nerve fibre has been
manufactured to take the place of one of our motor or sensory
nerves. What the American physiologist achieved was the

production in an iron wire of chemical changes providing a fair analogy to those observable in a live nerve through which a nerve impulse is travelling.

The iron wire is immersed in concentrated nitric acid, under the action of which a thin layer of oxide is deposited on the surface of the metal. On being again immersed, this time in diluted acid, no reaction takes place, and the wire is said to have become "passive". If the oxide layer is subsequently scraped at one point, the acid recovers its corrosive action, and the wire is "reactivated".

If a passive iron wire is immersed in a certain dilution of nitric acid and reactivated at one point, a wave of activation is propagated round that point in the form of a dark stain due to the reaction of the iron; but this activation diminishes as the wave spreads.

When we recall what was said above concerning the propagation of the nerve impulse the analogy is seen to be striking. Indeed, as Chauchard says, "the nerve impulse is therefore not a mysterious vital phenomenon but a physical process which can be reproduced in an inanimate model".

Nevertheless Chauchard adds that there remains an unknown factor, namely "the production of these electric charges when the living cell begins to function".

ARTIFICIAL FERTILIZATION

The supremacy of physico-chemical forces is so great, and the analogy between the behaviour of inorganic and organic matter so close, that even the initial vital act, the bringing into play of the potentialities contained in the egg, can be set in motion by mechanical means.

Fifty years ago Delage and Loeb brought about cellular division in the eggs of sea-urchins and star-fish by the use of sea-water of varying salinity, or of mechanical mixers. Just as Wöhler made urea without the help of liver or kidney, so in this case the spermatozoon is dispensed with, its place being taken by purely chemical action, or solely by physical impact.

In 1910 another step was taken. On this occasion the subject of the experiment was not a biologically relatively simple creature like a shell-fish, but the ova of a female rabbit. Pineus and Schapird succeeded in bringing about segmentation of the ova *in vitro* by freezing. It must be admitted that the phenomenon did not go beyond the first stages: nevertheless the experiment opens up startling possibilities.

Furthermore, the even more crucial point requires to be made that these biologists were experimenting with eggs which already contain within them the germs of life: we are far from having generated life by the employment of nothing but inorganic substances. Nevertheless it has been proved that the biological shock by which the male element activates the developmental potentialities contained in the egg has an undoubtedly close affinity with physico-chemical forces. Nevertheless, in normal circumstances the male and female nuclei must unite before further development may occur.

DUST ...

Thus we see that we are composed of the same inorganic substances as the material universe. We are fashioned from earth no less than the scientifically labelled substances contained in the chemist's bottle.

Not only do these substances make up our human bodies, but their interactions remain the same whether they take place in the test-tube or the human tissue. The molecular changes which are constantly going on in our blood and liver when we are thinking and willing are intrinsically the same as those produced and observed in the laboratory.

A great modern physiologist, Professor Morat of the University of Lyons, was fond of emphasizing this advance in human knowledge. At the beginning of his *Traité de physio-logie*[5] he writes:

> The century which is drawing to a close has been remarkable in the field of physical chemistry for far-reaching discoveries which seem to guarantee man's control of the forces of nature. Biology has made its contribution, and the living creature has been subjected to an analysis which has brought us a more accurate understanding of man, and endowed him with undeniable mastery. But our most valuable achievement has been the realization that the general laws governing the universe apply equally to man, forming the very foundation of his existence, and that physical determinism governs human as well as cosmic phenomena.

A block of stone falls out of the crane which is hoisting it to the top of a house, and carries with it the man working on the building: both events are governed by the same physical laws.

Yet there is a difference between the two which must be pointed out at the outset of our inquiry. Whereas the stone, on reaching the ground, remains a stone, and suffers no substantial change, what was a man one second before the accident is replaced by a corpse. Herein consists the gulf separating the stone from the man.

Yet if this be so, the question arises with even greater urgency: what then is this mysterious power by virtue of which we say that we are alive? We are in a better position to elucidate this problem now that we have become more fully aware of the material basis of our constitution.

[5] 4 vols., Paris, 1904–1918.

CHAPTER II

LIVING DUST

"Life is but a word meaning ignorance. When we apply the adjective 'living' to anything, we mean merely that we are dealing with a phenomenon of whose immediate cause and conditions we are ignorant."

This is the language of scepticism, the words of a dis-illusioned man looking back over a lifetime wasted in bio-logical research. Yet they were written by Claude Bernard himself, the father of modern physiology, in his *Introduction à l'étude de la médecine expérimentale*, and in a paragraph pungently sub-titled: "Scientific ignorance combined with certain illusions of the medical outlook are an obstacle to the progress of experimental medicine."

Bernard was obviously preoccupied with this problem, to which he frequently returned; no doubt because it seemed to him even more important than all those more tangible prob-lems which his experimental genius had succeeded in solving. His naturally speculative turn of mind—well illustrated in his photograph by Trinquart—was constantly reverting to the ultimate question: what is life?

COUNTERACTING THE DECOMPOSITION OF MATTER

The formula which we quoted above—"life is death"—is contradicted by another, equally well known and infinitely suggestive. It was employed by Bichat, whose short life (he died before reaching the age of thirty-one) left an indelible mark on the history of biology. The formula occurs in the opening sentences of his *Recherches physiologiques sur la vie et la mort*, published when he was twenty-eight years old, in which he makes a distinction which has become classic between the phenomena of "animal" life, involving sensations and movements, and "organic", or as we should now say "vegetative" life, involving the processes of nutrition.

"Life," says Bichat, "is the totality of the death-resisting functions." The casual reader may indulge in a smile of astonishment that a scientist should take the trouble to declare that life persists for so long as death does not prevail. However, Bichat's meaning is very different. His formula corresponds exactly to our quotation from Claude Bernard, and means that life persists only by virtue of the organizing power with which it resists the breakdown of the chemical molecules and physical forces of which it is composed. Left to themselves, these chemical components disintegrate and return to the dust from which they arose. Life itself is a builder, and from such materials it builds its organism.

Bernard himself, in a course of lectures on general physiology delivered in 1872, showed that he was in complete agreement with Bichat, and admitted no discrepancy between the two apparently contradictory formulas quoted above. He recalled that in his Introduction to the Study of Experimental Medicine he had himself used the words "Life is creation", while at the same time he took up once more his previous formula "Life is death".

Our quotations are designed to emphasize as strongly as possible the essential characteristic of life, which consists in a ceaseless striving to build up its specific substance from materials which, left to themselves, tend only to revert to the inanimate state.

In point of fact, the characteristic of every living creature whatsoever, from the most rudimentary to the most highly developed (and thereby the most complex), consists precisely in the unity which distinguishes it from, for example, a stone. The block of stone to which we referred, which preserves its identity after being broken or crushed, thus differs from even the simplest form of life. It is unnecessary to point out that when we cut a frog in half, the two halves of the individual frog do not continue to exist. A creature lives only by virtue of its "unity" or, to use the more scientific term, its "organization". In other words, it is characteristic of life to persist in the living creature, each of whose parts exists solely for and in the whole: every process at work in what may be called the individual chemical laboratory is directed towards one goal and serves one end.

Thus life, while maintaining itself by physical and chemical processes, belongs to a realm transcending both physics and chemistry.

Provided that successive chemical reactions take place, whether they nourish the organism or whether they end by poisoning or even killing it, chemistry is content: the whole process follows the laws which the chemist has discovered and formulated. All is determined by the laws of chemistry, regardless of the consequences. It pays no attention to the vital interests of the individual which, if the truth must be told, are of no interest to it.

Consequently it is not, in the last resort, chemistry that will provide the solution of our problem. The dominant feature of every living creature, i.e. its internal cohesion, can only be understood, not by analysing its component parts but by studying its life and observing its behaviour.

INTERNAL COHESION

Now the most striking characteristic of the living creature is its unity, the way in which every detail is coordinated with a view to maintaining the life of the whole. Whereas the stone cares nothing for the future, the living creature, even if still in the unicellular stage, strives to preserve its form; a result which it achieves by its own appropriate activity. It is this cohesive force which is the specific feature of life.

It is true that when the naturalist observes amoebae or infusoria he can distinguish certain features in which their appearance differs, such as the nucleus, the protoplasm, the vacuoles and the vibratile cilia. By using more powerful instruments he can distinguish within the nucleus various bodies whose greater or less capacity for absorbing colouring matter renders them visible, and still smaller bodies beyond these. Up to this point the work of the naturalist seems to resemble or to be identical with that of the chemist who pursues his task of breaking down molecules. He parts company, however, with the specialist in analytical chemistry in so far as his observations lose all significance the moment he breaks the subtle link which binds every detail into a coordinated whole.

Cuvier was right when he defined life as "a vortex pursuing a constant course".

This cohesive force, already observable in simple forms of life such as the bacteria and protozoa, shows itself even more clearly when we are made aware of the persistence of life in fragments of tissue taken from organisms of great complexity. This experimental feat was achieved by Alexis Carrel and Burrogs in 1912 at the Rockefeller Institute in New York, when they succeeded in keeping alive a fragment of the heart of a chicken embryo. The living fragment was taken with infinite precaution from the live animal, immersed in the nutritive liquid known as Ringer's solution, and placed in a culture receptacle, in the same way as the bacteriologist seeds a culture medium with bacteria. But the peculiar feature of this experiment was that, instead of preserving life in a whole creature, as in the case of the bacteria planted like seeds in an appropriate medium, Carrel and Burrogs on this occasion started with a fragment of an organism as functionally complex as the heart of a chicken. This tissue cutting remained alive, multiplied, and even retained its contractile properties. Finally, they succeeded in replanting a slip of the culture, just as the bacteriologist keeps alive a family of bacteria for an indefinite period.

In 1924, the twelfth anniversary of the experiment, the number of replantings had reached 2,254. Carrel told me himself that if all the living matter produced by the original cutting of less than one cubic millimetre had been preserved, it would have weighed several tons: it was only the outbreak of war in 1939 that put an end to its survival.

Better still, in 1913 Carrel obtained what he called "visceral organisms". With the characteristic virtuosity expected of him he removed from a live animal the viscera, i.e. the lungs, heart, and digestive tract with all its glandular accessories, and arranged them in a specially constructed container provided with an opening for the supply of air and food. Further openings were provided to maintain the supply of a chemical substitute for blood, and to evacuate the waste products. As a result, he found himself with a portion of an organism consisting solely of the viscera, severed from all connection with the central nervous system, and receiving only such nerve impulses as are sent out by the visceral ganglia. Nevertheless life went on, at any rate for a certain time.

It therefore appears that any organism, considered as a whole, contains within itself local centres where life can to a certain extent persist in latent form. The experiments of Professor René Leriche have increasingly focused attention on the local activities which continue when an organism like the human body is attacked by disease. The modern study of cellular pathology opens up new horizons for the surgeon and the physician.

Nevertheless, all these wonderful discoveries, so far from

obscuring the unity which, at a higher level, synthesizes all these more or less localized activities, serve rather to throw even more light on what is finally the most striking peculiarity of the living creature. That characteristic was noted centuries ago in the "Hippocratic Collection" of the works of the Greek physicians, where we find (in the περὶ τροφῆς) the famous formula: "All things converge, all things conspire, all things harmonize; all the parts in the whole, in particular all the parts of every part, work together to a common end."[1]

PRE-HUMAN FORMS OF LIFE

This internal unity, already observable in the unicellular organism, acquires increasing prominence as we ascend the ladder of life from those relatively simpler forms to the anatomically and physiologically most complex organisms.

In this book we are principally concerned with man, since our subject is human nature. But the full significance of the elaborate mechanics of human life can be appreciated only by setting man in the wonderful framework of animal life revealed to us by science.

For this great law of the coordination of separate functions with the organs through which they act asserts itself still more clearly when it is viewed in the context of the forms assumed by life at the present day or at this or that moment of the past. The problems of the origins of life and of evolution are dealt with in other volumes of this series. We need not therefore discuss here the questions raised by the origin of the splendid vital force which we are seeking to define, or the methods by which the forms it assumes succeed and give birth one to the other.[2]

[1] The celebrated works of Hippocrates are admittedly from the hand of more than one author. See C. Singer, *Greek Biology and Greek Medicine*, Oxford, 1922.

[2] See George Gaylord Simpson, *The Rhythm and Methods of Evolution*, New York, 1949.

We are not concerned here with the attempts to provide an explanation, whether by the evolutionary hypothesis or some other theory. What cannot be denied is the progress exhibited from relatively simple forms of life to the higher animals, and particularly the mammals, culminating in man. It is impossible to avoid the conclusion that this diversity of forms is governed by design since, in considering them in their totality, we seem compelled to speak of a progress, an ascent towards ever more perfect organisms, until we reach man, who seems to be the goal at which life is aiming.

It is true that here and there in the course of evolution we find ourselves in a blind alley. Such checks in the march of progress must raise troublesome questions for the palaeontologist engaged in reconstructing the story of evolution from the available evidence, and must plague the biologist who is seeking a plausible explanation for such apparently aimless experiments. Yet, if we have the necessary detachment to take a comprehensive view of the story of life, we should be wilfully closing our eyes if we failed to perceive in it the workings of a vast plan directed to a final goal—man.

COORDINATION OF FORMS AND CORRELATION OF FUNCTIONS

But there is more to marvel at than the evolution of anatomical structures and functional adaptations. What is yet more remarkable is that even the smallest change of detail in the living bodies arranged by science in ascending order does not take the form of a mere addition to the organism which in other respects retains its identity. The slightest structural modification can take place only if corresponding improvements are simultaneously effected at other points, and if at the same time some transformation of function allows the new factor to take its place within the whole.

Science, dispensing with technical terms, would say that a

reptile cannot grow a wing unless the whole organism is transformed from top to bottom in such a way as to make the new factor viable. In Pascal's fine phrase: "The slightest movement is of consequence to the whole universe: one pebble changes the entire sea." Nevertheless, the reaction of the sea to the pebble dropped in the water is slighter than the smallest anatomical change or physiological variation in an "organism". It is precisely in this correlation of forms that the specific characteristic of the organism resides.

We owe the discovery of this law to one of the greatest of French scientists, Cuvier. Born in 1769 in Montbéliard, which then formed part of Württemberg, he became at the age of twenty-six Professor of Anatomy at the Natural History Museum in Paris. In his *Leçons d'anatomie comparée* he says: "Every organism constitutes a whole, a closed and unique system whose parts intercommunicate and cooperate towards the same end by a reciprocal action. No one of these parts can change without all the others changing also. If an animal's intestines are organized for digesting raw meat only, then *it is also necessary* [our italics] for the animal's jaws to be constructed for devouring its prey, its claws for seizing and tearing it, its teeth for biting it to pieces, and the whole arrangement of its limbs for pursuing and capturing it."

It was the facts, the anatomical observations, and not any preconceived idea, which led Cuvier to formulate this great principle which gives pride of place to the concept of organic unity. L. Vialleton, who in the course of time was to carry on Cuvier's work, describes his method. "Having grasped the importance of the locomotor apparatus in the animal kingdom, Cuvier made it his point of departure; but instead of first making a complete study of the skeleton and then passing on to the muscles, he refused to make a separation between such closely linked parts of the body. He studied the spine and the skeleton of the trunk socket in conjunction with their respective muscles, the bones of the limbs in conjunction with theirs."

This initial concern to preserve functional unity intact led to some remarkable discoveries. "Thanks to this method, every bone acquires a definite meaning, while its various parts are explicable[3] by their function. So complete is our understanding of the bone that even when, as frequently happens, it is found isolated or in fragments in a fossil bed, it can always be recognized."

This law of the correlation of forms has proved extremely fruitful in application. Cuvier was able to carry it to the extreme limit without meeting any flagrant contradiction from the facts. Starting with a few fragments of bone unearthed in the course of excavation, he ventured to reconstruct the entire skeleton. He was guided by the requirements of the principle he had himself discovered. Thus a certain detail seemed to him to involve a certain form, while another involved a certain anatomical arrangement. Finally, when subsequent excavation provided the anatomists with a fossil bony structure, it was found to correspond to Cuvier's imaginary model.

This result is of such importance, and such a source of pride to the human intellect, that it may be justly considered one of the greatest of scientific triumphs. Cuvier, like all pioneers, may have occasionally erred in points of detail; but it remains true that it is his method that has inspired his followers to add an improving touch here and there. The law of correlation between forms and structures remains one of the most characteristic features of the living creature.

APPARENTLY USELESS ORGANS

Nevertheless, there is one objection which might be brought

[3] This word should be emphasized. We are here in the realm of science, which does not confine itself to stating a fact, but provides a reason for it.

against Cuvier's law. It derives from the presence in living
creatures and particularly in man, with whom we are more
immediately concerned, of anatomical structures which we
are driven to conclude are useless.

Before pronouncing judgement, however, great caution must
be exercised. It is not so long ago that a biologist included in
his list of rudimentary organs the pituitary gland. We now
know that the pituitary gland constitutes perhaps the most
essential centre of neuro-hormonal coordination.

It remains nevertheless true that the human body contains
certain organs whose removal by surgical means certainly
leads to no disorder. Moreover, this was never the case with
the pituitary or the thyroid glands, since, apart from their
valuable endocrine activity, an operation performed for the
removal of a goitre, for example, was found to give rise to
serious disturbances. On the other hand, removal of the ton-
sils or the appendix was followed by no biological effects. If,
therefore, their removal should one day be proved to affect
some functional activity, it can safely be said that the consequences would be of the slightest.

Are we then to conclude that the presence in our bodies of
these anatomical structures is meaningless, as is undoubtedly
the case with certain muscle fibres situated near the outer ear?
It is at this point that comparative anatomy can put forward
an explanatory hypothesis. These organs, rudimentary or useless in man, are shown to perform an important and undeniable function in the evolution of other living structures. The
arguments drawn from this discovery by evolutionary theories
are well known. Though it would be illogical to claim from
these facts a definite proof of filiation of species, yet we are
driven by the observable facts to conclude that living creatures
are biologically linked; while the appearance of the living
forms throughout the course of time suggests the idea of a
general plan of advance.

THE ANIMAL WITH HANDS WHO STANDS UPRIGHT

We see from the above how comparative anatomy and general zoology help us to understand the nature of man, considered as a member of the family of living creatures. Like his fellows, he is characterized by the specific feature which distinguishes inanimate from living matter, i.e. an internal unity, a coordination of the parts in the interest of the structure of the whole.

From this point of view man may be correctly defined as the animal with hands who stands upright. We shall have more to say concerning the part played by the hand in the practical activities of the human mind: but this is not the point of view we adopt in this second part of our inquiry. For the moment, we confine ourselves to the biological consideration of man as a living creature; and in so doing, we discover in him the same characteristic which distinguishes the other creatures, namely the correlation of forms.

In order to make the point clear, let us for a moment imagine a creature provided with that marvellous tool, the hand, with its extremely delicate structure and combination of flexibility and strength in action; but a creature condemned by its general anatomy to support itself permanently not only on its feet, but also on the anatomical system composing the extremities of its upper limbs. However ridiculous the supposition, it demonstrates in striking fashion how the possession of hands would have been of no use to man, had he not been able at the same time to stand upright; for it is due solely to the upright stance that the hand, that splendid instrument, enjoys complete freedom in use. If man had been unable to stand up firmly on his lower limbs, his hand would have been almost useless: he would not be the famous *homo faber* dear to the psychologists.

Yet in spite of the evident truth of this proposition, we should do well to stress all its implications. The upright stance implies and includes an entire anatomical structure and unity of functions. It requires not only a perfectly vertical alignment of the lower limbs, but also a tibio-tarsal articulation securing the erect posture, and knees which, unlike those of even the most highly developed primates, are not in a permanent state of semi-flexion.

The internal necessity which thus shapes the lower limbs and dictates the position of the pelvis, at the same time determines the structure to be assumed by the spinal column with its scaffolding of superimposed disks for securing the upright posture, maintaining balance in walking, and allowing free lateral and vertical movement to the head.

Now let us look beyond the skeleton, and examine the arrangement of the muscles, the coordination of the blood-vessels which supply them with food and carry away the waste products, involving in the process an appropriate structure and behaviour for the heart and, in addition to all this, the system of nerve fibres which convey to every part of the body the orders issued by the instinctive or voluntary impulses. More and more do we come to grasp, beneath all this baffling complexity, the wonderful coordination and the astonishing cooperation between the smallest parts and the whole, the adjustment of every detail with a view to securing and maintaining unity.

Every day the factory-hand tending his machine, the reader taking a book from the library shelf, the orator underlining his thought with a gesture, are all unconsciously bringing into play an infinite realm of structural and functional correlations.

Moreover, when this cohesion is disrupted by sickness or accident, the victim, if he has the courage to face rehabilitation, finds that various compensatory systems help him to form new anatomical-functional combinations. He himself is not clearly aware how his recovery is brought about: all he perceives is that whenever he makes a conscious effort to perform a certain act, some area or other of his organism experiences more difficulty in contributing its part. The physiologist, with the means of observation and control at his disposal, will then point out to him that in future, when he wishes to use his hand, a supplementary effort will have to be made by some muscle of, for example, the back, or by some conductor of nerve impulses, or some brain centre.

FUNCTIONAL SYNERGY

Thus we see that functional is supplemented by formal co-ordination. Or rather, we are confronted with one and the same reality, which presents itself now in its material aspect (the organs described by anatomy) and now as an active process coming within the field of physiology.

At the beginning of this book we gave a picture, from the point of view of chemistry, of the Odyssey of a mouthful of food swallowed in the course of a meal. For convenience of observation and description, our account made a distinction between the phenomena of molecular decomposition and the totality of functions on which these phenomena depend. But in point of fact the mucous lining of the stomach or intestine is unable to secrete the specific digestive substances at the right moment unless they can extract from the blood-stream the substances required for the manufacture of an adequate supply of sugar. It follows that two things are required. First, the circulatory system must function correctly (a circumstance which in itself carries far-reaching implications) from the motor action of the heart to the pulsations of the smallest arteries. Secondly, the other chemical "factories" distributed about the body must also play their correct part of providing the blood circulating through the digestive cells with the basic materials they require to carry out their manufacturing activity. If any change occurs at any other point of the organism, the digestive mucus is unable to fufil its task. Conversely, if the supply of mucus is deficient, all the other functions of the body are impeded. The body is a cosmos in which a breakdown in one part throws all the rest out of gear.

Such is our passion for Cartesian lucidity and logical classification that science, faced with the portentous and baffling enigma of this perpetually self-regulating machine, has allotted to certain parts of the body, certain groups of organs, the rôle of conductor of the orchestra. It is to the nervous system in particular that science has assigned the complicated task of maintaining, and therefore of perpetually re-establishing, a state of equilibrium which is constantly liable to be overthrown, and which can be preserved only if the disturbance is not merely slight but instantly remediable, and a state of harmony restored. Moreover, this prerogative assigned to the nervous system is in complete accordance with the facts, provided we recognize and emphasize that this great regulative system can only function—can only do its job—in everyday language—if it is itself provided with suitable nourishment and protection by the whole of which it forms a part.

It is well known that modern physiology connects this regulative action of the nerve centres and their sensory and motor fibres with certain glandular organs which, instead of discharging the products of their chemical activities outside the body, pass them into the blood-stream: they are known as the endocrine glands. The ever increasing importance attributed by biology and medicine to these glands is due to the fact that they are constantly contributing their share of the complex of interacting forces at work within the body, and that they have a marked effect on the successful functioning of the regulative nerve centres, playing the part, in fact, of controllers-in-chief.

Yet these glands, like the nervous or any other bodily system, are not exempt from the general laws of physiology: their activity depends on the proper functioning of the liver, kidneys and muscles.

The human mind finds difficulty in grasping and expressing in words this total unity and interdependence of parts: it is happier when engaged in the task of definition and delimitation. It is therefore all the more necessary to continue to emphasize this characteristic, the distinctive feature of living creatures.

ADAPTATION TO THE ENVIRONMENT

This internal harmony which we have noted as one of the peculiarities of living creatures, this constant tendency (one might almost call it determination) on the part of each separate species to achieve this end, goes hand in hand with a capacity of adaptation to the environment. As a matter of fact, these two characteristics are closely connected, and make up a whole which cannot in practice be split up. Here again it is the human mind which makes distinctions, and is unable to proceed except by the methods of analysis.

The influence of the environment on life is obvious. Without the environment which will provide the necessary food, warmth and shelter, no living creature could survive. The fact is undeniable, and is scarcely worth mentioning. But the statement has a further implication. If the individual, and *a fortiori* the species, is to survive, he must be able to modify his previous behaviour in this or that respect. It follows, first, that such changes must not cause too great a disturbance, since life is subject to limitations whose infringement entails death; and secondly, that the individual must possess spontaneity of reaction and a willingness to refrain from attempting the impossible. If the necessary compromises can be worked out, life will be maintained. Its forms and modes of expression will not be exactly the same as before the effort was made, but the changes effected will ensure survival.

The fundamental concept of adaptation is universally admitted, and is constantly confirmed by the observable facts.

There is, however, a difference amounting to a violent cleavage of opinion when we attempt to discover the mechanism through which the compromise is effected. We found ourselves using words which imply an almost deliberately guided process; but not every biologist is willing to ascribe a teleological significance to the phenomenon. It is not the concern of this book to discuss this question, which is both a biological and a philosophical problem.

Even more serious are the problems raised by the concept of adaptation for the scientific explanation of the evolution of living forms throughout geological time. The inquiry into the possible methods of adaptation led to the writing of such books as Lamarck's *Zoological Philosophy*, published in 1809 in Paris, where the author held a professorship at the Natural History Museum, and Charles Darwin's *Origin of Species*, published in 1859 and presenting the results of twenty years of laborious research.

This is not the place to describe and discuss the various theories of evolution. However, although these theories must be accounted no more than hypotheses, since no retrospective experiments can ever be carried out, we now have at our disposal such ingenious methods of observation and such powerful scientific resources that hitherto unsuspected facts are being brought to light. For an example we may quote the enormous increase in certain living species after being introduced into a new and favourable environment, as in the case of phylloxera, the Australian rabbit and the Colorado beetle.

In recent years naturalists have witnessed the colonization of the Atlantic coasts of Europe by a Chinese crab. The story is as exciting as a novel. This crab, *Eriocher sinensis*, which is widely spread in the Far East, particularly on the western coast of Korea, has the capacity of living in fresh water, at least for a period of its life. In 1912 some fishermen, much to their astonishment, caught in a tributary of the river Weser an animal which they failed to recognize—the universe not having yet yielded up all its secrets. They sent it to the Hamburg Zoological Institute, where it was identified, though the riddle of its arrival in Europe remained unanswered.

At any rate, from 1923 onwards the crabs multiplied to such an extent that in 1928 400 kilos were caught, while in the following year one man alone caught 1,000 kilos. About the year 1935 it was calculated that 500,000 kilos of crabs were caught in the Elbe: today they are to be found as far away as Rouen, or in the water-courses of the Rhine, 500 miles from the sea. The fact is that the fecundity of the crab is enormous, a female of average size producing nearly 300,000 eggs, while a larger specimen produces more than 900,000.

This rapid increase led inevitably to a disturbance of the vital equilibrium between the new-comers and the other denizens of the sea and streams, particularly the fish whose spawn was eaten by the crabs. At the same time the crabs attacked the water-works by undermining their foundations.

This vivid real-life story illustrates the importance to biology of the "struggle for existence" to which Darwin attributed a decisive rôle in the history of living creatures. Moreover, what is true of one species taken as a whole is equally true of every individual.

Consequently when, as in this book, we consider the human individual, and attempt to distinguish his characteristics *qua* living creature, we must include among them not only unity but the necessity and capacity of functional adaptation to the environment.

VARIATIONS AND RHYTHMS

In addition to the living creature's interaction with the environment, his spontaneous striving to maintain his unity, and the complex of functions by which he achieves the constant coordination of the various biological tasks he has to perform, there is yet another characteristic feature of life: it follows certain rhythms.

The human organism is subjected perpetually to external influences which would upset its equilibrium, were it not for the astonishing functional ingenuity devoted to restoring the balance. The maintenance of life and, what is more important, of health, is in no way comparable to the state of inertia obtaining between the two empty pans of a pair of scales. So long as we remain alive, every event provokes some vital reaction. Variations in atmospheric pressure and in temperature, solar and other forms of radiation to which we are constantly subjected, the mere act of breathing or swallowing a mouthful of food or lifting an arm—every one of these factors is calculated to endanger our biological unity in the absence of an immediate and active response on the part of the organism. So much is this so, that wherever we look we find a period of tension immediately counterbalanced by a period of relaxation. Surplus and deficiency succeed one another without pause, and our stability, however real and necessary, is preserved not along a straight line but along a sinusoidal curve.

The extent of variations differs according to the function involved and according to the individual temperament. Some people's constitutions are more stable than others', some people's cardiac rhythm remains the same throughout the day, while that of others accelerates for the slightest reason. There are people whose spirits, together with the receptivity and response of the vago-sympathetic nervous system which conditions them, show little variation throughout the day, while others, who are fit for nothing when they get up in the morning, feel better and better as the day goes on. There are people whose long periods of euphoria, or even excitability, have to be paid for, as it were, by weeks or months of depression, a condition to which psychiatry has given the technical name of *cyclothymia*.

Our "biological self", to borrow the expressive term used by Professor Marcel Sendrail to designate our fundamental unity, consists in a constantly repeated victory over the disturbances which threaten it, with the result that we are in a state of constant change. This condition is a factor and a sign of health, provided that the changes obey the law of ebb and flow and observe a rhythm. Hence, no doubt, the need men feel to create rhythms themselves, as exemplified by the recession of planes in a building, the arrangement of volumes and colours in a picture, and even more obviously by processions, dancing and above all music.

In view of what has been said above, there is no need for us to analyse the biological mechanisms by means of which these compensating rhythms are sustained. We need only remember that in every nerve, for example, a phase of excitability is succeeded by a reactive phase of quiescence. In brief, the nervous system which looks after our vegetable life, and controls the working of our viscera, lungs, heart and intestines without involving either our consciousness or our will in the process, is composed of two great antagonistic "power-houses", the pneumogastric and the sympathetic systems, one inhibitory and the other excitatory, designed in association with each other to ensure that neither inhibition nor excitation shall go beyond a certain limit. The two are so closely combined for carrying out their complicated task that they are known in scientific terminology as the vago-sympathetic system, vagus being another name for the pneumogastric nerve. To this system is assigned the whole duty of regulating the rhythms of visceral innervation.

It should also be noted that the endocrine system, whose functions, as we have seen, are associated with those of the vago-sympathetic, exhibits the same phenomena. Each of the glands of which it is composed secretes certain highly specialized chemical substances, which it passes into the blood stream to affect the other organs of secretion or the vegetable nerve centres. These chemical messengers are called hormones, from the Greek word meaning "to excite". But the secretions produced by each gland are found by analysis and experiment to contain substances of opposite properties, which are distinguished by the addition of the plus or minus sign. Here then, once more, we find a particularly striking example of the compensating alternations which we call "rhythms".

GERMINATION, BIRTH, GROWTH, DECLINE AND DEATH

In addition to these hourly, daily and seasonal rhythms, there is another feature which characterizes the constitutional unity of living creatures. Every living creature we encounter today was born from an original cell which went through a process of repeated division terminating in the production of an organism. This applies at any rate to the great majority who have passed beyond the unicellular state and are composed of innumerable cells. Every one of them, after a period of growth and maturity, is doomed to exhibit signs, first of diminished vitality and then of old age. Every one of them will come at last to die.

In the less highly developed species, such as the unicellular forms of life, parturition is effected in the most rudimentary fashion; yet scientific instruments of observation reveal an infinite complexity in this method of producing offspring. The division of even the most insignificant mother-cell, when it attains maturity and gives birth to two daughter-cells, constitutes a world in itself: every advance in biological research brings to light more astounding details. The microscope enables us to watch the break-up of the nucleus, the arrangement of the chromosomes preparatory to their taking up a position at opposite poles, and the gradual separation of the mass of protoplasm.

We shall have more to say later on about how, in man, instinct, which in the animals counts for everything, is transformed by the emergence of feeling, and how the capacity for love—in the true sense of the word—is one of the essential characteristics of the human species. For the moment, we confine ourselves to the biological phenomena as observed by the naturalist, and merely point out that among the distinguishing features of life is the fact that it is handed on by reproduction, and that the offspring develops from a single cell, called an egg.

The child will one day grow up. But what is growth, and what are the mechanisms and centres which control and regulate it? In the process of growth we recognize the operation of the same nervous and endocrine systems, involved in the same harmonious symbiosis. Here we can do no more than refer the reader for further details to the works of recognized authorities.[4]

The curve of life mounts, at a rate varying with the species, to a plateau, where for a period it is subject only to such minor variations as we have noted above. At last the moment arrives when the accumulation of waste products outweighs the supply of nourishment. The general vitality diminishes, old age betrays itself by the general slowing down of the assimilative apparatus and by the correlative weakening of all the bodily functions, and the warning signals of the approach of death are multiplied. Finally the living flesh reverts to dust.

Yet this lifelong process of variation, this slow ascent to the plateau and descent from it, operate in a being who, even while undergoing change, preserves his basic identity. And when a living creature occupies a place on the biological scale characterized by the complexity of organization displayed by the human organism, this unity becomes all the more apparent.

[4] See Bibliography at the end of this volume.

THE PRINCIPLE OF UNITY

We now find ourselves faced once more with the question raised at the beginning of our inquiry: what is this "force" which guarantees or maintains that essential unity which differentiates a living creature from a lump of matter which can be broken up with impunity? Its nature remains a mystery in spite of all our researches. We may indeed go further, and say that the more we seek to understand it, the more it appears shrouded in mystery.

But a great step towards clearing up the problem is taken when we perceive more clearly that we are dealing with something that cannot be fully "explained". Etymologically, to explain means to unfold: the Latin word *explicare* means to spread out what was previously folded up. But it is precisely at this point that we become most aware that Life (with a capital L) is not amenable to this unfolding and spreading out process, which is possible only when we are dealing with inorganic matter.

The human mind, as Bergson pointed out, is so constructed as to be ill at ease except when dealing with "things", precisely because "things" can be measured. It is to intuition that we must have recourse if we wish to understand life.

Nevertheless, we are always inclined—tempted would be a better word—to reify life, that is, to treat it as a thing, when that is precisely what life is not. What word are we then to use?

Claude Bernard, in the inaugural lecture of his course on general physiology delivered in 1872, made the following memorable statement:

> The idea of a cause which directs the evolution of the phenomena of life is probably the first to enter the mind, and appears irresistible when we consider the strictly determined evolution of the numerous and admirably coordinated processes which enable an animal or a plant to survive throughout its lifetime.

When we see an animal leave the egg, and take on step by step the form and constitution both of its parents and of its own future offspring; when we watch it performing simultaneously a vast number of overt or hidden actions whose concurrence seems expressly designed to keep it alive and well; when we consider all this, we cannot help feeling that all the separate phenomena which combine to make up the animal's life are guided and coordinated by a cause.

It is to this cause, considered as a guiding force, that the term physiological soul or *life force* [Bernard's italics] may be applied. The expression will serve, provided it be defined and not stretched to cover too much. It is a mistaken interpretation that has, so to speak, personified the vital principle and turned it into a kind of builder of the whole organic edifice.

Bernard then severely criticizes what he calls the "vitalists" for calling in a force outside and foreign to the organism—a supplementary force, to put it bluntly.

Is this a just criticism of the vitalists, particularly of the Montpellier school to whom the label is almost automatically applied? Certainly Stahl, the originator of the conception, never fell into the error so rightly condemned by Bernard; while Barthez does not equate the "vital principle" with any force external to the organism. This, however, is a point of merely historical interest. What matters is Bernard's conclusion, which no biologist can afford to neglect:

Granted the fact that the phenomena of life are linked to physico-chemical processes, the essential problem remains unanswered; for it is not any accidental conjunction of physico-chemical processes which fashions the individual to a predetermined plan, and brings about the wonderful harmony characteristic of the behaviour of living creatures. [Then follows the famous passage:] The living body reveals an organization, a kind of disposition which must on no account be overlooked, since it constitutes what is certainly the most prominent feature of living creatures. Admittedly this idea of organization is not satisfactorily expressed by the word force:

but in this context what matters is not the word but the undeniable reality of the fact. . . . Every individual and every organ appears to conform to a pre-established plan, with the result that although each separate bodily process obeys the general laws of nature, yet each, when considered in connection with the others, displays some special relationship, and seems to be directed by some unseen guide along the path which leads it to the place it occupies.

Let us recall some of the words we have used: force, unseen guide, physiological soul. Surely, when we use the word "animated" of the body to distinguish it from "inanimate" matter, we are in reality talking of the "soul".

Physiology, which makes us aware of what our "dust" is from the moment when it becomes alive, opens a window on to a something beyond matter, to which we must now turn our attention.

CHAPTER III

DUST QUICKENED BY MIND

Before embarking on a new stage of our inquiry, we must pause for a moment and recapitulate what we have already learned. By so doing, we shall be in a better position to appreciate the nature of the task which lies before us.

Our preliminary investigation has demonstrated that man and matter are built up from the same chemical substances, and that our bodies are subject to the same physical forces as those which govern the composition of inorganic matter.

We then considered man in his biological aspects, and were led to perceive that the dust of which he is composed is stamped, as it were, with a distinguishing mark that may be expressed in the one word life. It is true that in man the bodily aspects of the vital processes have been brought to a higher degree of perfection, and perform a greater number of tasks with far greater efficiency. Nevertheless, they are at bottom identical with those displayed in the behaviour of other living organisms. To such an extent is this the case that an observer who remained content with the illumination provided by the several sciences might be tempted to confine man within the limits of the animal kingdom. In so doing, however, our observer would, perhaps unconsciously, be submitting to the unwelcome tyranny of those very sciences.

When the chemist, as already described, studies the substances which make up the living creature, and discovers the laws which determine their biological reactions, he is deliberately disregarding the life which animates that creature.

Such a procedure is perfectly legitimate, given the requirements of the scientific discipline to which the chemist is submitting: chemistry, as such, is concerned with nothing beyond the combinations of indifferent molecules. Under these conditions it is scarcely surprising that life does not yield up its secret to the chemist: it is not life he is looking at. But if our expert presumed, on the strength of his competence as a chemist, to express an opinion on the nature of life, he would be exceeding his acknowledged competence in his own field.

Again, the biologist does no violence to sound logic when, after employing the methods appropriate to his branch of science, he finds that they shed no light on what it is that distinguishes man from the animals. A great biologist of the last century exclaimed: "I have never come upon the soul in the course of a surgical operation"; whence the conclusion has been drawn that we have no soul. The statement is strictly accurate. In using his knife to dissect a corpse, the anatomist will assuredly not find the soul. Yet it would be wrong to equate the data derived from a dead body with the results yielded by observation of a live man.

The situation is completely transformed if we cease expecting physiology to give us the last word concerning human nature; if we stand back, or rather stand high enough to take in the totality of aspects presented by the living human being. The "animated body" is now seen to be not merely a stage for the exhibition of biological phenomena; not merely an organism which grows, reproduces itself and dies; not merely a creature with legs and hands capable of carrying out an infinite variety of movements; but a creature who thinks, speaks and loves, and possesses freedom of choice in action. All of which leads to the recognition that the "vital principle" revealed by biology in the animal becomes in man a spiritual soul.

ADUMBRATIONS OF INTELLIGENCE IN THE
ANIMAL KINGDOM

All the same, it does not follow that no animal behaviour deserves to be ascribed to "animal intelligence".

Even in the simplest forms of life, which might even be called rudimentary in comparison with the marvels of structure and function exhibited by, for example, the insects or the higher vertebrates, life expresses itself in behaviour which suggests the idea of a certain freedom of choice, and consequently of a rudimentary consciousness. We are no longer in presence of the "vegetative life" exemplified by the glorious scent of a rose-bush, the luxuriance of an apple-tree, the majesty of a pine or an oak. This is a form of life which struggles to obtain food and avoid danger. And the same type of behaviour can be observed even in unicellular creatures.

These "tropisms", to give them their technical name, were subjected to an extremely ingenious examination towards the end of the nineteenth century, largely as a result of the publication of J. Loeb's *Der Heliotropismus der Tiere*. The observations recorded in this book showed that animals steer towards the light in obedience to purely physical events. Such reactions are purposeless, since the animal is drawn towards the light even when its action entails disastrous consequences, a commonly quoted example being the moth which is consumed in the flame of a lamp. As a matter of fact, the problem is far more complicated than Loeb supposed. Later researches, particularly those of Jennings, have shown the impossibility of reducing all the behaviour of even rudimentary animals to simple mechanical processes. Before long the lower forms of life exhibit a tendency not to approach but to avoid; and today increasing emphasis is laid on these "avoidance reactions", which have been given the name of "pathies."

As we ascend the scale of living creatures the evidence for

a knowledge of the external world (if we may use such an anthropomorphic expression) and for a certain freedom of choice becomes more and more striking. We are now in the astonishing realm of instinct, where it is difficult to select from among the innumerable actions carried out by animals with a view to maintaining the exercise of their vital functions.

Among the most amazing of these are the feats of certain migratory species. There are, for example, birds like the wild geese which leave western Siberia at the end of autumn, fly over the Himalayas, and arrive in India after covering a distance of 2,500 miles: in the spring they make the return journey. Then there is the American golden plover, which migrates from Labrador to the Argentine Pampas, a distance of nearly 10,000 miles. Or there are fish like the herring, and better still the salmon.

The female salmon spawns towards the end of winter: she weighs about twenty-five pounds and lays as many as thirty thousand eggs. The egg is hatched, and by March the young salmon is nearly an inch long, though still incapable of movement and relying on food from the bladder attached to its stomach. At eighteen months it measures six inches and has developed into an expert swimmer. Two winters after birth the young salmon launch themselves on the current, facing up-stream, whereupon the entire shoal is carried backwards down the stream to the river and the estuary. By this means the salmon becomes adapted to increasingly salter water, and ventures further and further from the coast. On reaching the open sea it swims out to a distance of over twelve hundred miles, where it settles down to two, three, four or even five years of growth, at the end of which time it measures up to three feet six inches and weighs as much as thirty pounds. It then sets off on the return journey to the coast and up the river to the stream, leaping with astounding agility over bars and waterfalls. Finally, spawning takes place in the waters where the shoal was born.

"Instinct", we are told. The word covers a multitude of problems. Why does the salmon, unlike other species, leave home? How does it hear the call, first to the sea and then back to his native stream? How and why is it impelled to make such journeys, involving a complete upheaval of its biological equilibrium? Recent research suggests that changes in thyroid activity may play a part in these phenomena. But the riddle remains unanswered, and we are no nearer understanding how the salmon adjusts itself to each successive stage of its journey. We seem to be dealing with a kind of knowledge, an adumbration of the freedom of choice enjoyed by human beings.

There are other unsolved mysteries of the animal kingdom. As a result of a series of ingenious experiments, Professor Karl von Frisch of Munich has discovered the signals—which might well be called the language—employed by bees.[1]

Four dishes containing honey are placed at the four points of the compass round a hive. After a period of time which varies, one of them is discovered by a foraging worker bee. When the bee has drunk the sweetened liquid, it is marked with a coloured spot and allowed to fly back to the hive. Later on, more bees arrive and drink from the same dish, paying no attention to the others. What is remarkable is that the original forager does not return with the new-comers. We are forced to the conclusion that the first bee has told the later arrivals of the position of the dish. How is this accomplished?

By means of a kind of dance. The foraging bee executes at top speed a series of figures of eight at a greater or less angle from the vertical. The speed varies, and was found by von Frisch to be proportionate to the distance of the food. He then made the even more astounding discovery that the angle of inclination of the figures of eight corresponded to the angle

[1] Karl von Frisch, *The Dancing Bees*, Methuen, London, 1954, and Harcourt, New York.

described by two lines joining the hive to the sun on the one hand and the dish of honey on the other. Furthermore, again following von Frisch, the bees can be seen palpating, as it were, the abdomen of the worker bee: they recognize the scent of the flowers with which it is impregnated, and are thus made acquainted with the nutritive value of the flowers growing round the hive.

What is even more remarkable is that certain kinds of animal behaviour seem to presuppose the power of choice, and even of invention. We may quote as an example the experiments carried out by the German psychologist Köhler, whose apes managed to find out that a stick could be used as a tool to reach their food.[2] However, the intelligence of apes is a matter of common knowledge, and causes less surprise than the discovery that hens, which have the reputation of not being particularly intelligent, show glimmerings of inventiveness. Yet it is a fact that if a hungry hen is placed in a run open on one side and affording a view of a heap of grain through the wire fencing, she will continue to run up and down her imaginary prison until she finds the opening. Is her success due to chance? Her wild rushes to right and left, which continue for a considerable time before she hits on the opening, suggest to the observer that she is learning to explore and master the situation.

PRACTICAL INTELLIGENCE AND THOUGHT

Such elementary manifestations of intelligence reveal themselves in man, though they constitute only a part of his mental activity. Much light has been thrown on them by modern psychological research. They are commonly described by the term "practical intelligence", and attempts have been made, particularly in recent years, to follow the stages of their development in children.

[2] W. Köhler, *The Mentality of Apes*, London, 1927, and New York, Humanities Press.

Some scientists, such as the Kellogs, have carried out the bold experiment of rearing a young female chimpanzee for nine months in company with their own son, aged less than one year at the beginning of the experiment. Another scientist, Boutan of Bordeaux, has compared the intelligent behaviour of apes and children, and has found that the difference consists in the acquisition of speech. As soon as a child begins to speak, he works like a little man and no longer like an ape. Similarly, the greater the intelligence the harder it becomes to master a problem by the primitive method of trial and error. It seems as if the intelligence has an inhibitory effect on the instinctual drives, the higher status of the former being prejudicial to the efficiency of the latter.

Observations and experiments such as these lead to a juster and deeper understanding of the nature of human intelligence.

There is in particular one kind of activity, which has been aptly termed the "working intelligence", where the two branches of human intelligence, the practical and the abstract, form an exceptionally close partnership. Since Bergson led the way in rightly stressing the idea of man as "homo faber", it has been recognized that one of the characteristics of human beings is to handle things and use them as tools, thus exercising ingenuity in finding out their usefulness. The next and higher stage in the inventive process consists in constructing a machine for the mass manufacture of better designed and more efficient tools. This specifically human activity provides simultaneous employment for hand and mind. The hand manipulates, while the mind directs, extends and improves the movement of the hand, and is constantly engaged in thinking out new inventions.

It would be going too far to say that the mind creates, for it must be remembered that human intelligence cannot do more than transform existing material. Further reflection suggests that a better word than "create" would be "discover". The word, in fact, embraces a wealth of meaning.

Confronted with existing reality, the human intelligence is obliged to exert itself to probe and lay bare its mystery, with a view to turning it to the best account.

The smith learns his trade at the smithy. It is a true saying; but we should add that the man who has gradually mastered his trade at the smithy develops into something far superior to a smith. He has not only widened his understanding of the mass of iron he has heated and hammered, but by labour and experience has gradually acquired a knowledge not only of the world around him which he has learned to shape to his liking, but of the whole universe and the laws that govern it, from the atoms to the stars; a knowledge not only of his actual job but of the past history of the entire cosmos. He is master not only of things but of ideas. "Conceptual knowledge" has developed throughout the ages thanks to the exertions of the whole man, both mind and body.

Our living dust serves as a tool for increasing the knowledge of which we are so proud.

SPEECH AND ACQUIRED KNOWLEDGE

At this point there appears a specifically human phenomenon —speech, by means of which the transmission of knowledge becomes possible.

No doubt the bee can indicate to its fellow foragers the whereabouts of their food supply, but its powers of communication are limited to the transmission of this utilitarian signal. Nor does it appear that bees, since the far off days when man first domesticated them, have made any appreciable progress. On the other hand, in striking comparison, during the same period of time man has continued to grow in knowledge, owing to the ability of each generation to hand on its knowledge to its descendants. It is a wonderful story. Not only does the father teach his son to make fire, hammer iron and catch water; he transmits to posterity his hard-won store of more strictly intellectual attainments. From the rudimentary knowledge revealed by examination of the remains of palaeolithic man to the achievements of an Einstein or a Pasteur there is an evident progress, subject no doubt to unfortunate mishaps and set-backs, which constitutes the most characteristic feature of mankind. The animal species, on the contrary, have changed hardly at all.

In view of these facts, while it remains true that man may be described as an animal endowed with reason, it would be equally true to say that he is an animal who, while retaining approximately the same physical appearance as when he first appeared on this earth, has displayed an extraordinary development of intellectual capacity.

This progress he owes to his ability to speak, and—what amounts in the end to the same thing—to write. The anatomical and functional connection we have noted as existing between the hand and the mind is now seen to be analogous to the connection between thought and speech. If man possessed no more than manual dexterity, the power of shaping reality to his liking and making known his needs by gesture, he would never have risen to such a height above the other species of living creatures. His pre-eminence as the seat of Mind he owes to his capacity for expressing ideas in words. His progress throughout the ages is due solely to his ability to make marks suggesting sounds which embody abstract ideas.

SELF-KNOWLEDGE AND BEHAVIOUR

Moreover, the capacity to conceive abstract ideas by means of which he gains increasing control over his physical environment is not the only attribute of man. He also has the gift of self-knowledge, acquired by observing his own nature and behaviour, by turning on himself, as if reflected by a mirror, the light of his intelligence. It is worth noting that the word "reflection" is applied equally to the action of a ray of light and to the consideration of an idea in the mind.

Man thus appears as a creature capable of self-knowledge. Would to heaven that we might make greater use of this faculty, and benefit by what it has to teach us concerning human nature. We become worthy of the title of human being to the extent to which we take the time and trouble to understand ourselves, instead of yielding to impulse and being governed by our reflexes. Nor, in this connection, should we rest content with ready-made or parrot-like responses: our duty is to reflect (once more that word!) at leisure, and to keep a watch on ourselves in action and in thought.

Whereas an animal is entirely immersed in the business of living, the human mind is sufficiently in control to be able to look beyond the present moment and the passing sensation. It can not only watch itself at work, but can look ahead, imagine various courses of action, and weigh in advance the advantages and disadvantages of the possible alternatives.

It is at this point that man commits himself, and assumes prior responsibility for the consequences of his choice. He now enters the realm of moral values, which lies beyond the realm of practical affairs and the even remoter realm of intellectual and conceptual knowledge. Here, indeed, he will no longer be concerned with apprehending the convenience or the inconvenience of the task he sees awaiting him, or with estimating beforehand the pleasures and pains[3] which it will entail—an undertaking in which he might well be guided by instinct. When grave decisions are involved, the standard of comparison is between good and evil. More important than any intellectual considerations are those "values" which appeal to the conscience and are accepted or rejected by the will.

[3] We have no space here to discuss the complicated problem of human suffering, or the spiritual implications which differentiate it from the more exclusively physical sufferings of animals.

A SPIRITUAL SOUL

It is on this highest plane of all that man finds his freedom. At such solemn moments he asserts his claim to the noblest of human attributes. It is in such crises, decisive for the whole conduct of our lives, that we recognize in ourselves the essential quality that distinguishes us from the animals.

Surely this power of choice, which overrides the promptings of the flesh and the ingrained force of habit, can derive only from a source transcending the world of matter. It insists, and therefore proves, that the power which quickens the dust of which we are composed surpasses any purely biological urge. The soul which actuates our body bestows on us the gift of reflection and free will. It is a spiritual soul.

Here we approach the heart of the mystery of human nature. On reflection, we are bound to admit that only the mind is capable of forming ideas and concepts, and of evolving from them a philosophy to explain the universe. Only the mind can pass from the mere hearing of sounds to the appreciation of music. Only the mind can master and pass judgement on its own destiny, devote itself to noble ends transcending self-gratification and self-interest, and thus become a citizen of the world of immaterial goods. Nevertheless, when it is a question of conveying this fundamental truth and expressing this spiritual fact, the terms we employ remain, in spite of every effort, smothered in metaphors drawn from the physical universe. In vain do we strive to disentangle our conception of the mind from terms applicable to the description of things. Inevitably we find ourselves speaking of the mind as if it were a pre-existing object installed like a guest in the body.

It follows that, whenever we attempt a self-portrait, we are doomed to remain outside ourselves, so to speak. It is difficult to explain our own nature—and we have already remarked that etymologically to explain means to unfold, so that we are once more driven to employ a spatial metaphor. The difficulty is increased when we attempt to understand how our indwelling mind is destined for immortality. Strive as we may, we cannot help imagining "a something" which will survive us; whereas what is actually required of us is the realization that what survives cannot possibly be a material substance.

Nevertheless, since we have a mind our immortality is certain. Only the language of poetry or music can give us a glimpse of that supramundane world thronged with the souls of all who have gone before us. It needs a Beethoven, in the *Et vitam venturi* of the Mass in D, to picture in the surging waves of a tremendous fugue the unending procession of the heavenly cohorts.

THE ORGANIC CONDITIONS OF THOUGHT

The human soul, though spiritual in essence, is nevertheless imprisoned in a body. This never-to-be-forgotten truth was expressed in immortal words by Pascal. "It is dangerous to make man see too clearly his equality with the brutes without showing him his greatness. It is also dangerous to make him see his greatness too clearly, apart from his vileness. It is still more dangerous to leave him in ignorance of both. But it is very advantageous to show him both." "Man is neither angel nor brute, and the unfortunate thing is that he who would act the angel acts the brute."[4]

If the reader—to take him as an example directly illustrating the point—were to imagine that in following our discussion he were performing an "intellectual" or "mental" act, he would be greatly mistaken: his whole body is involved. It is obvious that his eyes are engaged, and that our argument is not communicated directly to his "mind". Yet the eyes cannot possibly function in isolation, any more than

[4] Pascal's *Pensées*, Everyman Edition, pp. 111 and 99.

can the brain centres which receive the sensory messages falling on the retina. Retina, brain centres and connecting nerves must *all* be in the requisite condition to perform their physiological functions. This means that every one of these organs must not only be in perfect anatomical health, with tissues unimpaired, but must receive a plentiful supply of nourishment. This in turn means that the circulatory system which keeps them constantly supplied with food must itself be in a condition of perfect anatomical and functional health: a single damaged artery would sever what appears on the surface to be direct communication between two minds. It is not enough that the system of communications should allow the nourishing blood to carry life and strength to the smallest unit of the organism: the life-bearing fluid must contain the appropriate chemicals for producing local oxidation. Finally, it means that the supply of food carried by the blood must, at some previous moment of time, have been replenished by the digestion of alimentary substances.

Nor is this all. The digestive tract is lined by countless miniature chemical laboratories consisting of glands whose output can be maintained only by drawing from the blood and skilfully secreting the necessary chemicals. Once again in this process the entire organism is called upon to play its part. If the lungs are not working properly, or if the kidneys fail to eliminate all waste products, or if the central nervous system which coordinates the whole is itself out of order, the whole machine breaks down—and the reader who, as we pointed out, might appear to be performing a purely intellectual act, will totally fail to understand what is actually going on.

We are fond of saying, and with good reason, that a man thinks with his hands; and we have already remarked on the correlation between manual dexterity and the practical intelligence which, though adumbrated in the animals, attains the height of perfection in man. In the conception of what

might be termed the most "intellectual" thought, a gesture of
the hand sketches and in a manner shapes the idea.

It would be even more accurate to say that man thinks and
wills with his whole body and in the interest of the entire
machinery which keeps him alive. Thus, when the forces on
which his biological activity depends begin to fail, the working of his mind slows down in sympathy. The soul continues
to inhabit the body, but becomes its "prisoner". In Louis
Arnould's fine book *Âmes en prison*[5] nothing is more remarkable than Sister Marguerite's success in setting free the
mind of the blind deaf-mute Marie Heurtin. Such devotion
reappears in the skill displayed by all engaged in the splendid
work of rehabilitation of the disabled.

BODY AND SOUL

To the unreflecting reader our deliberate insistence on the
vital necessity for the intimate and indissoluble connection
between biological functions and spiritual activity might seem
to imply such a submersion of the soul in the body as to
represent the latter as the sole true cause of human life; a
conclusion which would involve confusing a condition with
a cause. We must now remove any possibility of misunderstanding on this point.

The difference between a condition and a cause was
pointed out by Claude Bernard in his account of Brown-
Sequard's well-known experiment with a decapitated dog. On
injecting blood into the vessels supplying blood to the brain,
it was found that the vital properties of the muscles and
nerves destroyed by the operation were restored. "These facts
strike us as extraordinary only because we confuse the causes
of a phenomenon with its conditions." After some further
very sensible remarks which we unfortunately have no space
to quote, Bernard concludes: "If intelligence is seen to return

[5] Paris, 8th edition, 1910.

to a brain or physiognomy replenished with the blood their functioning requires, it would be an error to conclude that the blood or the cerebral matter are the seat of intelligence."[6]

The sciences dealing with the living human being will continue to add to our knowledge of the degree to which the operations of the soul are dependent on the state of the body functions: they will never justify our treating the body as a cause in comparison with the mind which actuates the whole being.

"The right attitudes of men towards the works of the soul depend on the different attitudes of their bodies.". . . "Greatness of soul results from a sound bodily constitution . . . whence it follows that he who has a delicate sense of touch has a nobler soul and a shrewder mind." The author of these apparently materialistic statements is none other than St Thomas, who is giving new expression to Aristotle's dictum: "It is as absurd to say that the soul alone understands, as to say that the soul builds or weaves."

Although the truth of this proposition is proved by lifelong experience, it is only by the closest effort of attention that we can appreciate to what a profound extent this union of soul and body is characteristic of human nature. We are constantly bedevilled by formulas, which unfortunately separate one thing from another instead of helping us to distinguish between them. It is no doubt true that mind is not matter, the body is not the soul. Nevertheless, "the soul does not move the body, nor does the body move the soul, without the collaboration of that which is moved, each exerting an influence on the other."[7]

Thus, when we ascend from the biological to the mental (once more a spatial metaphor is unavoidable) we find physical and consequently carnal factors at work in even the most immaterial activities of the mind. And conversely,

[6] *Physiologie générale*, Paris, 1872.
[7] A. D. Sertillanges, *Saint Thomas*, Alcan, Paris.

descending from the spiritual to the organic, we find the soul (Latin *anima*) animating the chemical and physical reactions. The situation is summed up by Sertillanges in the following striking words: "From the point of view of chemistry everything in the organism happens as if there were no soul; from the point of view of life everything happens as if there were no chemistry."

In short, it is evidently the mind that is in control, through the influence it exerts on the biological conditions; while the latter, in their turn, promote or obstruct the activities of the mind. Even if the whole body were in perfect working order, the "intelligence", considered as a separate entity, can only work with full efficiency if we are paying attention—and attention is a mental attitude. A gesture or posture of the body reacts directly on the quality of mental activity. If we want to listen we must keep still. Every speaker knows that he has lost his hold on his audience as soon as they begin to shuffle their feet.

Later we shall examine the sacramental implications involved in this deep-seated awareness of man's unity.

LOVE AND THE UNITY OF MAN

A privileged example, to borrow a term from logic, of the incarnation of the soul and of the spiritualization of the bodily urges is provided by the passion of love. The graduated progress we have already noticed in our discussion of mental behaviour reappears in the ascent of living creatures from rudimentary forms of life to the summit attained by the human species.

Once matter becomes endowed with life it strives to perpetuate itself. But rudimentary creatures like the amoeba consisting of a single cell are necessarily reduced to dividing themselves to form two new organisms: and the metaphorical expressions "mother cell" and "daughter cells" are used simply for the convenience of the beginner in biology, to whom the technical term karyokinesis would convey little meaning.

One step higher on the ladder of living forms we come upon the phenomenon called conjugation. This process can be observed in certain infusoria, which themselves consist of one cell only. When two of these creatures reach a certain stage of maturity they embrace each other and exchange minute portions of matter: they remain, however, exactly alike in shape, size and biological composition, with nothing to distinguish one from the other.

It is only at a higher degree of organization and functional complexity that we find a differentiation of male elements, such as the pollen grain in a flower, from female elements, or ovules; moreover, these two vital organs can be present together in the same flower or in different flowers. At this stage of the general evolutionary process we arrive at the phenomenon of fertilization, which consists in bringing about germination by fusion of two sex cells.

In the vegetable kingdom fertilization is effected without any active participation on the part of the individual: the fertilizing pollen is either blown away and sown by a chance puff of wind, or else it adheres to the thorax or legs of some insect flitting from flower to flower. Roughly it may be said that the plant remains in a state of insensitive passivity.

On the other hand, when we come to the animal kingdom and the more highly organized forms of life we encounter an extremely dynamic force, the sexual instinct which impels the male and the female to pursue one another. Among the commonly quoted examples of the astonishing feats performed by certain species under the influence of this instinct are the pursuit of a mate over long distances by certain butterflies, and the migrations through rivers and seas of certain species of fish, an instance of which we have already described, which deserve to rank among the wonders of nature.

Side by side with this pursuit, in which a glimmering of choice can be detected, there gradually emerges a rudimentary type of more or less lasting attachment, until finally it seems natural to describe the facts in terms of the couple and the family.

But in animals the strength of the sexual instinct is so urgent that the creature who is mastered by it yields, not passively like a plant, but as if driven by inevitable fate. The individual in this case is subordinate to the species and to life: his sole biological function is to serve as a link in the chain of survival.

In the human species, the culmination of the evolutionary process, the same powerful instinct appears, bearing witness to our kinship with the rest of the animal creation, but transfigured now by an immaterial force which stamps us as belonging to the spiritual world. For man it is no longer a question, as for the majority of animals, of merely seeking a partner for the purpose of mating and satisfying the desires of the flesh: something infinitely greater is involved, namely a choice in the full meaning of the term. It is true that the choice includes elements of physical attraction and of desire for sexual union; but at the same time it admits spiritual elements deriving from the fact that the beloved object is He or She, a unique psychical and moral personality whose happiness means far more to us than our own. Now the passion which simultaneously illuminates the mind and rouses the flesh is called love; and the full miracle of love is revealed by the utterance of the word "You" leading straightway to the word "We", expressive of the union of two persons.

At that solemn moment when a man and a woman plight their troth for life, and at the also very sacred moment of complete physical surrender by which they seal their love, the living dust of which they are composed rises far above the evolutionary stage attained by even the most highly developed animal: it proves that its home is in the world of spirit.

From this exalted standpoint it becomes possible to explain the demonstrable fact that a human being, unlike an animal, loses nothing in status when in obedience to a higher call he voluntarily renounces indulgence of the sexual instinct. Whereas an animal which does not mate is looked upon as a kind of left-over, or even, as among the social insects, as an intruder to be liquidated, man may be defined as an "animal capable of chastity". Let it be clearly understood that by chastity we do not simply mean physical abstention from all sexual activity, which might amount to no more than selfish escapism and a denial of life, with all their harmful consequences. In our use of the word we include the spiritual outlook which transforms an act of renunciation into a sacrifice inspired by love. The heights attained by men and women who, in fulfilment of their vocation, renounce the joys of married life afford a fresh proof that our bodies are governed by our minds.

If further proof were needed, it is once more to the inexhaustible wisdom of love that we should apply. When a man and a woman exchange a lifelong vow, and celebrate their marriage by a physical union, it is already "their" as yet unborn child who is the object of their love, and whom they promise to cherish from this most sacred moment onwards. Just as the parents' love embraces both body and soul, so they have not only brought the child's body into the world, but long for the day when the fruit of their physical union will receive the gift of a soul. The mutual avowal "I long for a child by you!" proves that a spiritual overtone accompanies the natural urge to perpetuate the species.

This expectation of the consummation of love by the birth of a child brings us face to face with a profound mystery, which we must now examine.

COLLABORATORS WITH GOD

Metaphysics teaches us that physical union, which in the animal species suffices to ensure the handing on of life, in the case of human beings requires the creative intervention of God. From the purely physiological standpoint the biological act of mating is sufficient in itself to cause fecundation followed by the production of a new life. The nature of a pair of mating animals is completely and wholly expressed in their biophysical activities; whence it follows that the sum total of the life of which they are the carriers is transmitted in an equally complete and direct manner to their offspring. But in the case of human beings, whose bodies are quickened by an immaterial soul, the vital forces cannot by themselves give birth to mind. In philosophical terms, the greater cannot proceed from the less.[8]

Step by step we are led to the logical conclusion that the uncreated Spirit must itself be the author and creator of the new human cell resulting from the fertilization of the female ovum by the male spermatozoon. The original seed which is destined to develop within the womb is quickened by the actual direct intervention of God.

It is a wonderful moment when, thanks to her husband's love, the wife becomes a mother. We may go so far as to say that at that moment husband and wife enter in a partnership with God, who makes their physical union a pre-condition for the creation of this new human soul. Here we are at the very heart of the mystery of life, a mystery of whose accomplishment the parents, although it is brought about by their agency, are unaware, since time must elapse before the recognition that the mother's body has become the repository of a new life.

Much of our mortal life is occupied by everyday affairs;

[8] The philosophical problem is discussed by St Thomas Aquinas, *Summa Theol.*, I, QQ. 75–83.

moreover it is our duty to labour at the cultivation of the earth which God has given to us for our use and enjoyment. Otherwise we should wonder more at the hidden miracle taking place within the mother's body, and welcome it in prayer and meditation. Nor should we allow familiarity to diminish the tribute of silent adoration which is due to the presence and intervention of God.

That the dust of which we are made should be alive was already a cause for wonder. Now that, by virtue of the spiritual nature of the soul which quickens our body, the love which engenders a human being draws husband and wife into so close a partnership with God, we perceive how greatly the dignity of human nature surpasses all the marvels of the physical universe.

THE CREATURE WHO GLORIFIES GOD

Physically man is already lord of creation; but since he is a spiritual being, he is chosen from among all other living creatures to pay supreme homage to God. *Coeli enarrant gloriam Dei*, in the words of the Psalmist: the heavens tell the glory of God, and the words evoke an awe-inspiring vision of the star-strewn skies. The display of so many wonders of nature, the main stages of whose evolution we have already described, no doubt bears witness to the infinite power of the Creator, and reveals its inexhaustible range. But all material and natural events take place automatically, and this kind of mechanical or biological obedience constitutes an inadequate response to the divine majesty.

The fact is that the totality of material and biological forces merely paves the way for the appearance of man on the sixth day of creation. All that exists has no other purpose than to provide the means for man to live and to exercise the spiritual faculties with which his dust is endowed. The sublime words of the Bible, "Let us make man wearing our image and likeness", reveal the very purpose of God. Now, and only now, does the entire universe acquire its full meaning. For this new creature, made in the image of God, has the capacity to understand the Creator's plan, and to discover, through the increase in scientific knowledge, the laws which govern the courses of the stars, the multiplication of the forms of life and their evolutionary progress. It is through the human mind, highest of created things, that the heavens are finally enabled to tell the glory of God. Since man's appearance on earth there has been one creature capable of appreciating the infinite majesty of the starry heavens above and of the teeming world below.

It is with the mind that the children of Adam glorify the omnipotence of the Creator; but better still it is from the heart that they respond to his never-failing generosity. In spite of imperfections, limitations and weakness, they are invited to make a willing response to God's love; and the humble self-sacrifice which they are permitted to offer is the finest tribute they can pay to his sovereign majesty.

The divine call is addressed to each one of us, however lowly his station here on earth. Every hidden thought which is brought to birth within us is in the nature of a response to the call. But far more than our thoughts, it is every willing participation in the divine plan, every act of adoration and of obedience to the law of God, and better still even the faintest impulse of love towards him, that imparts a meaning to the whole created universe. In this way even the humblest of us may aspire to the title of a creature who glorifies God.

When we began to reflect on human nature, and noted at the outset that we are composed of dust, how could we have foreseen the sublimity of the duty our dust is called upon to fulfil?

But there are still more splendid heights to which the spirit must mount. The God of love invites us to share in his very nature. We must now give some account of the prospects thus opened out.

DUST AND THE CALL OF THE SUPERNATURAL

Our appeal so far has been addressed solely to reason and experience, and its validity would be accepted by any right-minded person of intelligence, even when unenlightened by the gift of faith. It is now our duty to enter the field of the supernatural, since our picture of human nature would be, as indeed it is, incomplete, if it took no account of the know-ledge derived from Revelation.

The "serpent" had told Adam, "You will be like gods." It was a false promise, in that it tempted him to yield to pride and disobedience, whereas in his original state of innocence he had shared directly in the life of God; not that this parti-cipation precluded his being an embodiment of mind, of that unity we have attempted to describe, composed of matter, of primordial mud and of the breath which quickens it.

The Fall deprived man of this unique privilege, before whose mystery our reason can but bow in uncomprehending humility. But Redemption by the Son, the very Word of the Father and creator of all things, restored to finite humanity the hope of eternal life.

Henceforth the souls of all whom God has blessed with faith, and who are made members of the Church through the sacrament of baptism, are invited to pass from the natural to the supernatural plane. Yet in so doing, human nature still retains that unity which we have found such difficulty in defin-ing. The soul of the baptized and confirmed Christian, though privileged by grace to become the temple of the living God, remains none the less both master and servant of all the biological functions.

This dependence of mind on body sometimes appears as a monstrous and humiliating form of servitude. For human beings, always tempted to ape the angels, are at the same time forced to recognize that, apart from the exceptional cases of the mystical union with God, their spiritual activities remain subject to physical conditions. Every honest Christian must admit that, with the best will in the world, he cannot prevent his bodily condition from interfering with his devotions. The depression, or still more the pain arising from a headache or a slight attack of indigestion, can hamper the soul in its aspiration towards God.

So much is this the case that, considering the matter from another aspect, we know from our own everyday experience as well as from the experience of the saints that a bodily posture can help us to lift up our hearts to our Lord. Pascal's advice to the would-be convert was to take holy water and fall on his knees. It is universally acknowledged that certain diets "elevate" and purify the mind. Hence the traditional rules of monastic asceticism, to which medicine, if it cared more for the spiritual side of man, might one day apply the methods of exact science. This is a point to which we shall recur later.

The same body-soul relationship underlies the institution of the sacraments. The Church, following the example of her divine founder, has always resorted to visible signs as the "matter" of the sacraments by which she imparts her treasury of grace. The water of baptism, the laying on of hands in confirmation, the administration of extreme unction to the sick, the consecrated bread of the eucharist—all these are material elements, employed because we are dust.

As soon as we perceived that this dust was quickened by a spiritual soul we were ready to treat it with the greatest respect. But now that our faith has taught us to look upon the body as the temple of God himself, we have all the more reason for treating it as something almost sacred.

On November 8th, 1952, Pius XII made a speech in Rome to eight hundred delegates to a scientific conference on sport and education. Not so long ago an ignorant person might have imagined that a pope could take only the faintest interest in such matters. Exercise and record-breaking and physical culture seemed to be rather a renewal of the paganism which sees only the animal in man, a more highly developed animal no doubt, but whose ambition ought to be confined to rediscovering the beauty of the classical athletes.

Pius XII, on the contrary, took the opportunity of reminding his audience of the Church's teaching concerning the dignity of the human body. But after paying tribute to its admirable physical qualities he added these words:

> All this is recognized and accepted by religious and moral philosophy. They go much further than this, however, when they teach us not to overlook the origin of the body, to which they attribute a sacred character of which neither art nor natural science can of themselves form any idea. The King of the universe, wishing to bestow a fitting crown on his creation, fashioned by one means or another from clay the masterpiece of the human body and breathed into its face a breath of life which made of it the dwelling-place and instrument of the soul. In other words, by means of the body God promoted matter to the immediate service of mind, thus bringing together and uniting, in a synthesis which our mind finds it hard to understand, the spiritual and the material worlds, not only by a purely external bond but in the unity of human nature.
>
> After being thus promoted to be the dwelling-place of the mind, the human body was ready to receive the honour of becoming the very temple of God, together with the prerogatives, and even more than the prerogatives, of all buildings which are dedicated to him. Bodies indeed, in the very words of the Apostle, are "members of Christ". "Surely you know," he says, "that your bodies are the shrines of the Holy Spirit, who dwells in you. And he is God's gift to you, so that you are no longer your own masters. . . . Glorify God by making your bodies the shrines of his presence" (1 Cor. 6. 19).

THE RESURRECTION OF THE BODY

Here is the corollary of what revelation teaches us concerning our nature. Pius XII continued:

It is true that the body, by reason of its present mortal state, shares the common fate of other living beings who are borne irresistibly to dissolution. But a return to dust is not the final destiny of the human body, since we know from the lips of God himself that it will be recalled to life—and this time to life everlasting—when the divine plan, which in its mysterious wisdom unfolds itself like the evolution of the vegetable kingdom, shall have accomplished itself on earth. "What is sown corruptible, rises incorruptible; what is sown unhonoured, rises in glory; what is sown in weakness, is raised in power; what is sown a natural body, rises a spiritual body" (1 Cor. 15. 42–4).

The Christian faith, founded on the testimony of the apostles announcing that the crucified Jesus triumphed over death, guarantees that in us also Life will triumph over sin and death. In the *Credo* of the Mass we repeat the words: *Et exspecto resurrectionem mortuorum et vitam venturi saeculi* ("And I look for the resurrection of the dead and the life of the world to come"). Pius XII shows us how this expectation of the resurrection of the body, reunited for the life everlasting to our soul, is connected with the dogma of the Assumption of the Blessed Virgin Mary. "The belief in the bodily Assumption of our Lady into heaven ought to strengthen and invigorate our belief in our own resurrection."

In the preface to the Requiem Mass it is expressly asserted: *vita mutatur, non tollitur*, our life is not taken away but merely changed. We are left in no doubt that all who grieve for their condition, which includes the certainty of death, are comforted by the promise of eternal life by reason of the blessed resurrection of Christ.

The Lyons liturgy adds further details by substituting, at the end of the funeral Mass, for the *Libera me Domine* the responsory *Credo quod Redemptor meus vivit, et in carne mea videbo Salvatorem meum* ("I believe that my Redeemer lives, and in my flesh I shall see my Saviour"). It matters little whether these words are a proclamation of faith by the survivors or are attributed to the Christian whose death we mourn. After asserting our belief in the life of the Redeemer, the Son of God who took our flesh upon him, suffered death like us, and rose from the dead, we go on to declare, in words of peculiar solemnity at such a moment, our conviction that we shall *see* him.

The majestic words, which are thought to date from the ninth century, expressly state *in carne mea* ("in my flesh").[9] Though we are obviously not entitled to call ourselves qualified exegetes we should like to understand these three words as an assertion that we shall see our Saviour in our flesh, and consequently with our eyes, which will themselves be raised from the dead.

[9] This responsory of the Lyons liturgy figures also in the Roman rite as the first responsory at Matins of the Dead. It is taken of course from Job 19. 25-6. [*Trans.*]

CHAPTER IV

PRACTICAL PROSPECTS

It now remains for us to draw certain practical conclusions from our study of human nature. We shall mention only the most important, in the hope that even a short summary may suffice to indicate their crucial significance.

TOWARDS AN INTEGRAL "HUMAN MEDICINE"

Let us begin by considering medicine. What effect will our findings have on the work of the general practitioner?

Since the patient, whom it is the doctor's task to attend and to cure, is composed of an indissoluble union of body and mind, medical science is under the necessity of making no distinction in treatment between his physical and his spiritual aspects.

Not that it is the doctor's business to act as a spiritual director, or to encroach on the special fields of the psychologist, the metaphysician or the sociologist. A medical man should confine himself to medicine, leaving the other specialists to shoulder their own responsibilities.

The physical, or as Descartes would say, the spatial world is not the same thing as the mental world, nor should the distinction between them be overlooked. Distinction, however, as Maritain has pointed out, is not to be confused with separation.

For the chemist, the methods of analysis are sufficient to provide an adequate knowledge of reality. When we come to study living creatures, biology is sufficient so long as we are dealing with such species as plants, which are sensitive to material stimuli such as heat and cold, but are incapable of feeling emotion. But in the case of an animal, complete biological knowledge is impossible unless likes and dislikes are taken into account. No one can get to know (which in practice means to control) a dog or a cat without allowing for the subtle play of instinct, or one might almost say without considering their feelings.

But human nature cannot be explained by abstractions: to understand a man we must observe him in action, and not confine ourselves to his physical behaviour, which is inevitably affected by psychical and spiritual considerations. Medicine is useless if it disregards the unity of the living creature. The term "human medicine", by insisting upon which we hope to emphasize this necessity, is less well known than that of psychosomatic medicine, which we owe to the Americans. Not that it matters which term one uses: what is important is what one does.

In drawing up a plan for the practice of medicine, we cannot rest content with the hackneyed conception of the relation between the physical and the moral. Instead of confining ourselves to the recognition of organic symptoms only, we should constantly ask ourselves to what extent they are the result of psychical disturbances, and how they in turn intensify or even give rise to mental disorder. We should aim at placing ourselves at the very centre of the whole human person. Unfortunately we lack the ability to concentrate attention on both panels of the diptych simultaneously, and in looking from one to the other there is a risk of the living reality being overlooked.

Besides, the situation in medicine is becoming increasingly complicated. It is not only that there is a gulf between psychiatry and the branch of medicine which is concerned with the internal organs such as the lungs, heart and liver.

In each of these two fields, the physical and the mental, which instead of being surveyed as a whole are inevitably treated separately, the phenomena are so complex that to examine them closely and to apply the increasingly more refined modern techniques necessitates a narrowing of the field of observation. This is the day of the specialist—of the pneumologist and the radiologist and of the laboratory test.

So we see that medicine, in other respects a noble branch of learning, is threatened with fragmentation and its possible repercussions on the health of each one of us.

OUR DUTY TOWARDS OUR HEALTH

It is not from professional bias or a desire to make exaggerated claims for the art of medicine that I maintain that we have obligations amounting to duties towards our health. Rather was it this conviction that led me in a direction which I certainly never foresaw in my days as a medical student.

If human life were not of infinitely higher value than animal life, we might modestly say that it is advisable to do everything possible to keep fit for the simple reason that sickness and suffering are extremely unpleasant things: we should not refer to obligations or duties. But at the present stage of our inquiry we are concerned not with unpleasantness or even pain, but with the whole activity of the human being, including above all his mental and spiritual behaviour. A "human" conception of health necessarily includes these immaterial facts.

Any misgivings that might arise from this extension of the accepted idea of health are dispelled by the following passage from a speech of welcome delivered by Pius XII on June 27th, 1949, to a meeting of the World Health Organization.

One point in particular has struck us in reading of your plans and your labours: namely the meaning, at once wider and deeper, which you attach to the word health. Health in your opinion is not something purely negative, as if health in general consisted merely in the removal of bodily disease and physical defects, and as if mental health in particular signified no more than the absence of any form of derangement or abnormality. Health is something positive, involving the spiritual and social well-being of mankind, and may consequently claim to be one of the conditions of universal peace and world security. . . . It follows that the question of health cannot be confined within the framework of biology and medicine, but must take its place in the sphere of morals and religion.

As a matter of fact no man can think clearly, control his feelings or exert his will unless his body is in sound working order. A slight headache can put out a philosopher. Pascal called attention to this fact, which he had himself experienced: conversely, his niece Marguerite Périer noted that her uncle got rid of a raging toothache by burying himself in a geometrical problem.

Our discovery of the influence exerted by the hormones on the functional activity of the nervous system is of the greatest significance as throwing light on the part played by biological factors in moral behaviour. It would be a misunderstanding of the unity of the human being to suppose that spiritual realities such as temptations, sins or virtues are disembodied events taking place only in the soul. They are undoubtedly, as we shall have occasion to repeat in even stronger terms, far more than manifestations of bodily activity, and it would be a most serious mistake to degrade mental life to the level of physical phenomena. At the same time we should be guilty of a disastrous and vicious form of presumption if we overlooked the share of the flesh—by which we mean the totality of the visceral functions—in our good or bad moods, our generosity or selfishness, our courage or cowardice.

Since then, in the already quoted words of St Thomas, "greatness of soul results from a sound bodily constitution", we are under an obligation, if we wish to acquire or retain moral self-control, to take care of our health: physical fitness becomes a "duty".

It is easy to make this assertion, but trouble arises in practice when we have to determine the limits of our duty. In fact it will not be long before we find ourselves asking the question: "Ought I, when faced with the necessity of making a painful effort, to count the cost and weigh in advance the risks I run in overstraining my physical powers? Or ought I to think only of the task set before me, of the resistance it is my duty to offer to evil?"

Some men, the weaker brethren, are inclined to coddle themselves, while others persist in overstraining themselves. It is easy to talk of laziness and courage, but it must never be forgotten that such defects or virtues are conditioned by the state of the body, and that to a certain extent a lazy man is physically incapable of exerting himself, while an energetic man is by nature highly charged.

God alone knows what blame attaches to the individual, and it is not for us to judge our fellow men. In our present no doubt imperfect state of knowledge we can at any rate profit from the assurance that Providence has provided us with the means of gradually modifying our physical behaviour, and of avoiding by appropriate treatment the harmful effects of this or that organic dysfunction. This knowledge and the power derived from it impose certain obligations on us.

MEDICINE AT THE SERVICE OF MIND

Such considerations suggest the possibility of a branch of medicine dealing with emotions—a necessarily modest claim, since our science is still in its infancy, though since the time of Galen a number of books have been written on the subject.

But there is one word, asceticism, which has come down through the ages charged with a rich accumulation of patiently acquired experience. The positive aspects of asceticism have

sometimes been overlooked in stressing the elements of re-
straint and self-denial implied in the word, whereas the truth
is that "mortification", to be effective to the body, requires
the observance of certain prudential rules, not to mention the
care to be taken in its practice.

Space does not permit us to quote the many passages from
the letters of spiritual direction written by such great authorities as St Francis de Sales and St Vincent de Paul, or from
some of the greatest mystics, full of the strictest injunctions
on the subjects of sleep, diet and rest.

There is material here for a medicine of the future which
will at last consent to devote itself to the care of the mind.
There is a vast field waiting to be explored in such matters as
diet and clothing, and in the healthy lay-out of offices, factories, private or conventual houses and recreation grounds.

On this foundation it might prove possible to build a technique of mental therapy. We are already familiar with
chemicals which have the property of sustaining the attention
and preventing failure of memory: we refrain from using the
word "drugs" for fear of tempting the unwary to fly to such
stimulants except in cases of genuine necessity and after first
consulting a doctor. The pharmaceutical laboratories are de-
voting more and more time to research: the antibiotics are
not the only sensational discovery of recent years.

It is therefore not altogether fanciful to imagine a day when,
thanks to our increased knowledge of the physical mechanisms underlying the emotional drives—among which due
attention will no doubt be paid to the part played by the
hormones—medical science will be in a position to moderate
the violence of the sexual and aggressive instincts.

This is not the place to discuss the means by which research
may be directed into these channels. The reader may, however, be reminded of the constant attention devoted to this
subject by Alexis Carrel, who in 1929 put forward a plan for
interesting one of the great religious orders in such a project,

an idea which led later to the foundation of the Carrel Institute for the study of human problems.

Unless immediate action is taken along these lines we may find ourselves confronted with biological research stations which, though nominally humanistic in purpose, are in reality no different from institutions devoted to the breeding and domestication of animals.

Anyone who believes that man is actuated by mind may object that our sketch of a "spiritual medicine" leaves no place for the concept of merit. But merit will consist in a man's resolve to submit to a regimen and follow a prescribed course of treatment, demonstrating by these positive acts his determination to pursue the good. It will consist in the generosity with which, once cured of his disability, he will devote himself to the service of his fellow men. It will consist in the recognition until his dying day that his virtuous aspirations were a gift freely bestowed on him, and that even in his sinful state he is capable of responding however inadequately to the infinite Love.

THE SACREDNESS OF LIFE

Human life, because it is quickened by a spiritual soul, is something sacred, and consequently attains to a far higher level than is reached by the animals. We have already remarked how, in the animal kingdom, each individual parent is subordinated to the interests of the species, and acts merely as a link in the evolutionary process. Each individual man, on the other hand, possesses a personality of his own, whose worth is derived directly from the Infinite Being who breathed into him the breath of life.

What after all does it matter whether an animal goes on living or not? Or whether a domesticated animal is fit and strong enough to go on working for its master? As soon as it is of no more use and costs more than it is worth, the slaughter-house is at hand to relieve us of a useless mouth that can no longer earn its keep.

Enough has surely been said to emphasize the obvious difference between man and the animals.

To whatever state of organic or physical decay he may be reduced by the ravages of disease, man still bears the divine stamp imprinted on him on the sixth day of creation. In this light it is clear that man is not the sovereign master of his own life, which was a gift freely bestowed on him by God, of which he will have to render an account. No human being has the right to kill himself wittingly and directly: neither bodily suffering nor disgrace can justify deliberate suicide.

For the same reason no man has the right to kill another, except when his own life is directly and wrongfully threatened, and he has no other means of overcoming the aggressor.

Nor is it permissible to put a man to death, even though he prays to be spared intolerable suffering. However repugnant such a strict interpretation of the moral law may seem, we must bring ourselves to understand the motives justifying it. These are, that the spiritual element in the sufferer is incomparably more precious than anything else he may possess, so that however frightful his agony may be, reason compels us to acknowledge that the survival of the spirit is the most sacred of all considerations.

The unaided reason might doubtless arrive at these truths, while perhaps shrinking from their expression. But a Christian is supernaturally aided in solving the problem. Euthanasia might be welcomed by anyone not enlightened by faith in Christ, the crucified Saviour. Considerations such as these help us to appreciate the redeeming value of humble endurance of affliction. Nevertheless we must remember, in repeating these enlightening truths, that only a tone of conviction inspired by unfailing love can prevent their becoming a cause of scandal.

A fortiori it is only the spiritual-minded who are strong

enough to withstand the confusion of thought which leads certain doctors to argue that death would be a merciful release for incurable congenital idiots. Any community claiming the right to pursue such a course, on the grounds that money devoted to maintaining incurables would be better spent on the healthy, would be committing a crime against conscience, which can be sometimes ignored but never silenced.

NEITHER HEALTH NOR LIFE CONSTITUTES THE HIGHEST GOOD

The imperative duty of preserving health and safeguarding life is suggested to us not only by reason but even more urgently by the Decalogue: yet there are other and no less striking circumstances in which natural and revealed morality combine to set a limit on its observance. It might seem that here we are faced by a contradiction.

Let us take as an example a husband and wife, as full of love for each other as it is possible for human beings to be. Since their affection has a physical basis, they are sexually attracted to each other. They know from their married experience that physical intercourse has a beneficial effect on both of them by gratifying and enriching their physical, emotional and spiritual life. Unfortunately, however, some physical abnormality may render a new pregnancy dangerous; or else, on a lower but equally momentous plane, the arrival of another child would overtax their strength and resources. Where, in these circumstances, does their duty lie?

The answer of the advocates of a neomalthusian materialism would be: "There is no problem at all. We have a whole battery of contraceptive devices guaranteed to keep you healthy and happy in body and mind: you have only to avail yourselves of them. All pain is unhealthy, including the pain of childbirth: get rid of your stuffy old prejudices."

If medical science, keeping strictly to its own field, were

asked what it thought of this advice, it would undoubtedly have reservations to make concerning the harmful effects of repeated indulgence in such evasive practices. Psychosomatic medicine has in fact called attention to a number of abdominal or nervous complaints induced by allowing the female organism to experience sexual relief, while depriving it from the beneficial effects contributed by the male secretions. To which our opponents, who are not concerned with moral issues, will reply that they have any number of drugs to counter the ill effects of such frustration.

It is no doubt true that medical science would condemn the habitual practice of contraception in severer terms than it would apply to an isolated act of indulgence. But morality cannot approve the deliberate and voluntary dissociation of marital intercourse from its normal result in pregnancy. Morality appeals to reason in condemning even a single resort to contraception as an unacceptable fraud, and invokes the teaching of revelation in pronouncing it a grave sin, which is especially to be deplored in a Christian since it profanes the blessings derived from the marriage sacrament.

It is therefore obvious that the honour and responsibility of guiding human conduct cannot be left to the doctor, though he can and should play a part in training mankind in the exercise of moral freedom and of fortitude in enduring hardship.

At the same time medicine is already making a valuable contribution in this field, one of the best examples of which is to be found in this very subject of pregnancy. Prolonged research by biologists and gynaecologists has in fact led to the discovery of a period during which the female organism is not apt for conception. Intercourse during this period implies no subterfuge on the part of husband or wife, who are in no way interfering with the normal processes of nature: they cannot be charged with acting immorally.

There is, however, one most important reservation to be

made. Morals, the teacher and guide not only of our acts but of our intentions, are entitled in the present case to look into the bottom of our hearts. Husband and wife have a moral duty to examine their conscience and to weigh, as impartially as possible, their motives for avoiding the fertile period. It is these ultimate motives which will finally determine the legitimacy or the selfishness of their conduct: it is for this inmost disposition of their hearts that they are to be held responsible.

* * *

These few examples are enough to show the great opportunity presented to a medical science inspired by a true conception of human nature. Not only can it bring its expert aid to the cure of the sick, but it can be of great assistance to all the other sciences which serve our vocation as living creatures made in the image of our Creator.

To avoid any possibility of misunderstanding, we must once more disclaim any intention of setting up biology and medicine as moral, social or political arbiters. Their rôle is purely that of a consultant. Nevertheless, because their pronouncements are supported by experimentally verified scientific facts, their opinions carry exceptional weight in the modern world. All the more reason why an increasing number of medical practitioners should devote themselves to the kind of work we have indicated above.

Now that we have come to the end of our inquiry and can sum up the results we have arrived at, we may see clearly what bountiful blessings flow from a knowledge of the facts of human nature.

Dust we are, but living dust, and we owe our life to the spirit within us.

SELECT BIBLIOGRAPHY

(An asterisk denotes a work by a non-Catholic author.)

BIOT, René, and GALIMARD, Pierre: *Medical Guide to Vocations*, London, Burns Oates, and Westminster, Md, Newman Press, 1955.

CARREL, Alexis: *Man the Unknown*, London, Hamish Hamilton, and New York, Harpers, 1935.

KÖHLER, Wolfgang: *The Mentality of Apes*, English translation by Ella Winter, London, Kegan Paul, 1925, and New York, Humanities Press.

RIEZLER, Kurt: *Man, Mutable and Immutable*, Chicago, Regnery, 1951.

SAUDÉE, J. de Bivort de la (ed.): *God, Man and the Universe*, London, Burns Oates, and Kenedy, New York, 1954.

*SIMPSON, G. G., and others: *Life: an Introduction to College Biology*, New York, Harcourt, 1955.

TAYLOR, F. Sherwood: *Short History of Science and Scientific Thought*, New York, Norton, 1957.

TAYLOR, F. Sherwood: *The Century of Science*, London, the Scientific Book Club, 1943.

W H A T I S F A I T H ?

IS VOLUME

6

OF THE

Twentieth Century Encyclopedia of Catholicism

UNDER SECTION

I

KNOWLEDGE AND FAITH

IT IS ALSO THE

2ND

VOLUME IN ORDER OF PUBLICATION

Edited by *HENRI DANIEL-ROPS* of the *Académie Française*

WHAT IS FAITH?

By EUGÈNE JOLY

Translated from the French by DOM ILLTYD TRETHOWAN

HAWTHORN BOOKS · PUBLISHERS · New York

First Edition, September, 1958   *Fifth Printing,* June, 1960
Second Printing, October, 1958   *Sixth Printing,* January, 1961
Third Printing, January, 1959   *Seventh Printing,* February, 1962
Fourth Printing, November, 1959   *Eighth Printing,* June, 1962

CUM PERMISSU SUPERIORUM O.S.B.

NIHIL OBSTAT

Hubertus Richards, S.T.L., L.S.S.

Censor Deputatus

IMPRIMATUR

E. Morrogh Bernard

Vicarius Generalis

Westmonasterii, die IX MAII MCMLVIII

The Library of Congress has catalogued this publication as follows:

Joly, Eugène, 1901–
    What is faith? Translated from the French by Illtyd Trethowan.
[1st ed.] New York, Hawthorn Books [1958]

    144 p. 21 cm. (The Twentieth century encyclopedia of Catholicism, v. 6. Section 1: Knowledge and faith)

    Translation of Qu'est-ce que croire?
    Includes bibliography.

    ———————

    1. Faith.   I. Title.
    BT771.J613   234.2   58–11592 ‡

CONTENTS

CONTENTS

TO THE SEEKER AND THE DOUBTER

These pages are dedicated to all those who are in search of God: to those who are willing to examine the atheism into which they have been led by the mental atmosphere around them or by their own reflection, to all those who will face the question "What if it were true?" with the honesty with which Christians sometimes ask themselves "What if it were not true?"

For these pages are dedicated also to those who question the faith in which they have been educated and brought up. I do not believe in the value of a faith which has never been questioned. I am afraid that it may be a mere "conformism". Whether one has been born and bred a Catholic or lives all one's life among atheists, conversion to Jesus Christ is something that has to take place at some time or other. It may take place at any age. Some people's arteries harden and they become old at twenty—old men are ever so much younger than they. The normal age for conversion to Jesus Christ tends to be between eighteen and twenty-five. But sometimes the bustle of life prevents people from putting to themselves the all-important questions until they are forty or fifty. To these men of riper age as well as to the younger ones the author would hold out a helping hand.

These pages are concerned simply and solely with *meeting the living God*. This is not a subject which falls naturally into "chapters". Really one ought to say everything at once. But since this is impossible, I shall try to approach the mystery from various sides in turn. I shall not make light of the difficulties which put off the unbeliever—they are often my own—but I shall try to appreciate them justly and to overcome them. So I ask the reader to be patient. A page at the beginning may perhaps not become clear until somewhere near the end; nevertheless the conclusions would not make sense without their premisses.

I have marked out the stages on a journey. The stages must not be confused with the journey itself, still less with its goal, which is God. And the stages themselves are described in a very summary way. At the end of the book—and in the course of each chapter—I have mentioned books which have helped me and which will help the reader to pursue this search for God.

I am certain that there is no man of good will who cannot know the joy and wonder of meeting the living God.

CERTITUDE, CERTITUDE, JOY, PEACE

THIS IS ETERNAL LIFE THAT THEY SHOULD KNOW YOU
THE ONE TRUE GOD AND HIM WHOM YOU HAVE SENT
JESUS CHRIST

CHAPTER I

WHAT IS FAITH?

Any honest conversation with an unbeliever is at the same time a great unhappiness and a great happiness for a Christian.

It is a great unhappiness, for the Christian knows all the misunderstandings which prevent the unbeliever from finding God in Jesus Christ, and the Christian is keenly aware of his own inability, not only to convert the unbeliever (he knows too well that this does not depend on him!), but simply to remove the misunderstandings. If one could say so without making the Christian seem "superior", I should say that his position is rather that of one who sees in regard to one who is blind. As far as hearing, touching, smelling and tasting are concerned, both men reach the same results. But the man who can see cannot make the blind man understand the transfiguration which his whole life would receive if he could be cured of his blindness. It seems that only the experience of sight could give to the blind man the enchantment of this world of light and colour.

But, unlike most physical blindness, spiritual blindness would be curable, if the blind man would cooperate. The unbeliever's good will would soon lead him to the light. The Christian is indeed well aware—for many reasons which will be explained later—that he cannot give the unbeliever faith. But he has often the quite special joy of showing the way and then seeing the extraordinary developments which take place in someone who is moving into the light. This growth which he witnesses is something which he feels to be entirely beyond him, and it fills him with stupefaction. A meeting has taken place between a soul and the living God; its effects are palpable, and its permanence guarantees its objectivity. All the Christian has done is to facilitate this meeting by leading the unbeliever out of blind alleys and informing him of the direction to take so that he may find God. It is in this spirit of fraternal help that I would pass on to my unbelieving brothers the indications which, through no merit of my own, I have received. Unbelievers sometimes seem to envy Christians (*you are lucky enough to believe?*), and it is hard to tell whether they are expressing admiration or scorn. Do they mean "you are living in a world from which I am unfortunately excluded" or "you are living on illusions which compensate you for the unfortunate realities which my intelligence and my sincerity force me to face"? Either way, the unbeliever declares that he has no "feeling" of these alleged realities which the Christian mentions. He is like a man who cannot share a friend's admiration and enthusiasm for some picture which seems to him ridiculous or at least insignificant.

This comparison brings us back to that suggested above. The unbeliever, like the blind man, lacks a faculty. He lacks "the eyes of faith". His mistake is to suppose that this faculty is innate and cannot be acquired. Just as the picture can become intelligible if it is looked at with a trained eye, so the realities of the faith become accessible through a certain sort of cultivation which I shall try to indicate.

*   *   *

But many unbelievers experience more than an incapacity to believe. They assert an *intellectual impossibility about believing*. The faith of Christians seems to them opposed to the deliverances of reason, and impossible for anyone who takes into account the findings of science. There are many types of mind among such people, and we may choose two of them for special consideration.

The Marxist claims to know how religious feeling comes to birth and develops. It is an epiphenomenon which can have a beneficial or a harmful influence according to circumstances, but which has no more objective validity than any other illusion. The Marxist is interested only in the consequences which religious sentiment may have on the historical process: he will foster it, tolerate it or oppose it, according to the political situation of the time. Obviously we cannot discuss it with him on these terms. Marx's penetration in other fields need not be questioned. But in religious matters, so long as the Marxist remains wedded to "scientism", he will really lack the faculty which enables one to perceive faith's realities. He must first be brought to take up a genuinely scientific attitude to the universe. The first quality required of a thinker is a willingness to submit himself to the real and not to mutilate reality so as to make it fit some theory based on only a part of reality. The theory, for example, which assimilates light to the radiation of particles is false because it explains only some and not *all* of light's properties. The Marxist must *recognize* that the history of life is just as much an uprising of conscious-ness as physico-chemical growth, and that spiritual energy is primary in the universe.[1]

A chemist who refused to admit the special properties of radioactive bodies, on the pretext that these bodies do not obey the laws of other bodies so far known to us, could not claim to be a scientist. A historian who does not admit the special char-acter of the Judaeo-Christian *fact*, and of the *fact* which is Jesus Christ in particular, cannot claim to be a scientist. And there is more to it than this. Modern physics would not have been born if physicists had dug themselves in and insisted on regarding radioactivity as an anomaly. In the same way, a truly scientific attitude must not merely admit the Christian "pheno-menon" but must consider whether the examination of these facts does not shed an extraordinary light on the human

[1] Cf. the first part of P. Teilhard de Chardin's *Le Phénomène humain* (Paris, 1955). [An English translation of this book is projected.—Trans.]

phenomenon as a whole, and so on the whole universe. Without this adaptability to *facts*, there can be no scientific spirit in any proper sense of the expression.

Much subtler is the familiar attitude of the agnostic: "What do I know? Surely the world is greater than the knowledge which I have of it? But I cannot hold as true what my intelligence cannot master."

This seems to be Jean Rostand's position[1]:

> It is one of my certitudes that intellectual dissatisfaction is our lot, that we must resign ourselves to live—and to die—in anxiety and darkness. When, after millions and millions of years, our race becomes extinct on this earth, man will still be ignorant.
>
> (But) I do not believe that man has any other means of knowing at his disposal except his reason. . . . I cannot take seriously the suggestion of a "revelation" supposed to have been made to our ancestors in the distant past.

The modesty, indeed the humility, of this attitude demands respect. The door is not closed to possible realities, which are simply supposed to be beyond our reach. It is then just a question of discovering whether these realities which faith proposes to us are really inaccessible for our minds. Two remarks are called for:

1. The witness of others can enable us to reach what is outside our own purview. I cannot see the skyscrapers of Manhattan from Paris, but witnesses assure me of their existence. "No man has seen God. The Son has given us knowledge of him," says John. Why not? I shall explain in the following chapter how God has revealed himself through historical events, the most important being the event which is Jesus Christ —events which are not lost in "the distant past" of which Jean Rostand speaks!

2. I think that agnostics minimize the capacity of our intelligence, that it is capable by its own power of discovering at least God's existence, and so of knowing God after some fashion. That really requires a considerable development, out

[1] Jean Rostand, *Ce que je crois* (Paris, 1952), pp. 14, 15, 75.

of place in a little book like this which is concerned not with theodicy but with faith. I shall allow myself only a few brief indications to clear the way for faith. The proofs of God's existence given by St Thomas Aquinas preserve all their force. And they seem to reduce to a single proof which the Doctor presents from different points of view.[1] The world does not contain within itself the reason for its existing. Nothing explains to me its origin and its life. If it had existed from all eternity, it would not appear to me any less "absurd". I cannot make sense of it unless I make it depend on a Being which does find in itself the reason for its existing, which exists of itself, *Ens a se*. Lachelier was saying that in a formula which is only strange at a first reading:

The world is a thought which does not think itself, dependent upon a Thought which does think itself.

Can we go further and verify this "induction" somehow? Lecomte du Nouy claims to make God's divinity, as it were, palpable for us. He established, for example,[2] by working out the probabilities, that the mere appearance on our planet of a molecule of protein would require 10^{243} milliards of years (1 followed by 243 noughts) whereas the earth has existed for only two milliards of years. I prefer to keep clear of such demonstrations, which involve a very uncertain extrapolation of what has been verified in our time for a certain restricted field of nature. Unfortunately—or fortunately—there is no possibility of finding God at the conclusion of a piece of purely scientific reasoning. But it is possible to discover in the evolution of the world, in the uprising of life, in the growing complexity of living beings and in the development of consciousness which accompanies it, a creative movement or *élan vital* as Bergson (less exactly) would put it, which is, so to speak,

[1] An account of them which is as intelligent as it is succinct will be found in *Foundations of Thomistic Philosophy* (London) by P. Sertillanges.

[2] *L'Homme et sa destiné* (La Colombe, 1948), p. 42 and elsewhere.

the shape in which St Thomas Aquinas's "first mover" presents itself to our modern eyes.[1]

This proof becomes more intimate and more persuasive when it applies to men, the axis and the apex of cosmic evolution. This creative movement which is at work throughout nature is seen in ourselves as an exigence for the fullest and finest development of our nature. Each of us has had this experience of a "duality":

> A will which commands and another which must consent. One which invites us, urges us on, seeks to fill us in order that we may grow—and one which gropes its way, and tries either to join itself with the other or to free itself from it. This intimate duality is the very drama of our moral life. We experience it as a struggle, a tearing apart; or as a harmony and a consenting. It is the deepest of our experiences.[2]

It is this "creative movement" (which we perceive in our inner life as we have discerned it at work in nature) which we call "God". But it must be carefully noted that this "energy" is quite different from what we call electrical energy, atomic energy, etc. . . . We are now concerned with a personal or personifying energy which raises life towards "personality" and never ceases to move us as persons. This exigence of infinite life, of continual transcendence, which puts us in the way of our destiny, and carries us indefinitely beyond ourselves, cannot be lower in the scale than ourselves. We are persons, and so this energy must be itself personal—or rather super-personal. In fact it must be *Somebody*—an intelligence and a will of a higher order.

God is not an abstract absolute. He is Somebody, Somebody who moves us while at the same time leaving us entirely free, Somebody who constantly requires of us a further development —and one which we can refuse. And how could we feel ourselves to be both dependent on someone and at the same time

---

[1] Paul Claudel has given us a very fine poetic translation of this in his *Légende de Prakriti* (Figures et Paraboles, Paris, p. 120).

[2] O. Lemarié, *Etudes de psychologie religieuse*, p. 225.

free unless this someone loves us? It is because God is love that we are at the same time totally dependent on him and totally free, and because we must live by him and for him in a dependence of love which enables us to receive everything from him without ceasing to be free.

Have we gone beyond what our unaided reason could discover? It is difficult for a Christian to know what effect his faith has had upon the movement of his thought. But I think that this same journey can be undertaken without faith. My present aim, however, is not to bring the reader to a natural knowledge of God (although I recognize that the human reason is capable of it). It is only to remove an obstacle and to show that God is—at least—possible, and even probable.

But the God of faith is not the God of the philosopher and the professors; he is Jesus Christ, as Pascal wrote on that night in 1654:

> God of Abraham, God of Isaac, God of Jacob,
> not of the philosophers and the professors.
> Certitude, Certitude, Experience. Joy. Peace.
> God of Jesus Christ. . . .
> This is eternal life that they should know you,
> the one true God and him whom you have sent
> Jesus Christ.
> Jesus Christ.

But the "not" of the second line must not be understood as a "negation" but as a choice. The God of the Sage and the God of the Saint are the same God; but by faith it is in Jesus Christ that we find God. This revealed God offers the soul infinite depths which reason alone would not suspect and which drive from Pascal's mind any question of a philosophical search for God.

*   *   *

With these preliminary remarks behind us, we may now reply to the question asked by the title of this chapter: What is faith? To have faith in someone is to rely upon him and to recognize what he tells us as true in virtue of the confidence which we have in him. The child believes what his mother tells him. The disciple admits as true what his master teaches him, because he has faith in his master.

We do not speak of faith unless the reality which we are to reach surpasses our own powers of discovery, unless we are obliged to rely on the witness of some competent person.

Christian faith is of this kind. I shall leave in the air the question about the powers of the unaided reason in this matter of knowing God. In any case the knowledge so gained will be very limited. What reason cannot tell us of God we ask of "God's witnesses", and in particular of the supreme witness, Jesus Christ. To have faith is to have confidence in God's witnesses, and above all to have confidence in Jesus Christ, and so to stake one's life on Jesus Christ.

This definition is not exhaustive. But it has the advantage of being clear and of avoiding a number of possible misunderstandings.

Faith is not a "feeling" which we either have or have not by instinct. It is an act of the intelligence which requires, in order that we may have confidence in Jesus Christ, guarantees that this confidence is deserved. It is also an act of the intelligence which tries to understand the message of Jesus, to grasp its coherence and its value.

It is also and necessarily an act of the will, for the will is necessary if this inquiry is to be pursued. It is equally indispensable for making our lives follow the direction in which Christ leads us, for life is known only by living it and love only by loving. Nevertheless this part played by the will does not in any way detract from the lucidity of the intelligence; on the contrary it makes it possible. The alpinist cannot get to know the mountain without effort.

The mountain, in this connection, represents all the historical events by which God has spoken to us, from Abraham to Jesus Christ. The intellectual effort which is now demanded of us is that of studying these events and seeing that they do contain a message. It will be also and above all a critical study of the person of Jesus of Nazareth; we must see whether we have the right to believe this man who claims not only to speak in God's name, but to be himself God.

CHAPTER II

GOD HAS MADE HIMSELF KNOWN

All philosophers agree in describing God as the Wholly Other, and so as the Unknowable. Pascal said: "If there is a God, he is infinitely incomprehensible, and we cannot know what he is." Certainly we can know what he is only in relation to ourselves, or more precisely what we are in relation to him. We can know nothing of his essence. We can only affirm that he exists, for without him the world would be impossible. It is correct to maintain that the "Unknowable" is the only divine name. St Albert the Great called God the "unnameable".[1]

We can know God only if he sees good to make himself known to us, to lift the veil, to reveal himself and speak to us. As opposed to de Vigny cursing "the eternal silence of the divinity", I have faith in a God who has spoken and continues to speak to me. That is the boldest and most certain affirmation that a Christian makes.

How does God speak? Where can we hear this Word? The Word of God is quite different from any human word because it is effective, bringing to pass what it says. Unfortunately (or fortunately) our words do not alter the course of events. It is quite otherwise with the Word of God of which the Bible tells

[1] Cf. Sertillanges, *Foundations of Thomistic Philosophy* (Sands), Ch. 3; or Daniélou, *Dieu et Nous* (Paris, 1956). [English Trans., *God and Us* (London, 1957).]

us, *dixit et facta sunt*. So God will speak to us by actions, by facts and events.

Creation is God's first word, an eternal word. "The world is a sign by which God signs to us. Through the universe, God himself is revealed and shows himself."[1] But above all God has spoken historically. He has intervened in the events of human history. He plays a decisive part in the history of Israel until the day when the very Word of God took flesh in Jesus of Nazareth, and we heard with our own ears, saw with our own eyes and touched with our own hands the Word of life.

The reader who is in a hurry had better leave out the rest of this chapter and go on to the next in which we shall discuss the discovery of God in Jesus Christ. But sometime or other he will have to review this long process by which God willed to make himself gradually known to men, with all the cautious delays of a wise teacher, so that we might learn, one by one, the attitudes which we ought to take up in his regard. We watch God's initiative and man's fumbling search for him, bound up with one another, throughout the course of eighteen centuries. We can give only one proof that this is not an arbitrary and imaginative interpretation of this long "sacred history", but it is a sufficient one: "The Bible makes an extraordinary impression on the historian: the contrast between the humble beginnings of Israel and the potency of the seeds, or rather the explosives, which it contains; its concrete shape shrouded from the outset in the loftiest beliefs; then its stately expansion, its confident though hidden progress to a boundless and unpredictable end: nowhere can be found anything in the least like it".[2] But it is not my business to write apologetics. My purpose is only to go over the stages of a discovery, to show how it can be made once more.

*   *   *

[1] *Eléments de doctrine spirituelle* (A.C.J.F.), 1st series, No. 3, which cannot be too highly recommended.

[2] de Lubac, *Catholicism* (London, 1950), p. 81.

THE GREAT STAGES IN THE REVELATION MADE TO THE PEOPLE OF GOD

We know scarcely anything of the slow development of man during the hundreds of thousands of years which followed his appearance on earth. No doubt we shall never know how he sought God and how God helped him. Our "sacred history" is relatively of quite recent date. It begins with Abraham, the father of all believers. Here—probably in the eighteenth century before Christ—there is a starting point and an absolute beginning which marks a stage definitely achieved (just as there will be a series of absolute beginnings which mark stages definitely achieved throughout the history of Israel). At this epoch there is a solemn entrance into (recorded) history on God's part.

Abraham presents us with an entirely novel situation in that a man is now conscious of being in a special relation with the one, true and living God and of being associated with him in a task which will embrace in the end all the nations of the earth. The precise way in which Abraham "experienced" God is of no great importance. We need not take literally all the imagery of the sacred text. But what is certain—the events of the following eighteen centuries guarantee it—is that Abraham underwent an authentic mystical experience. The essential religious values, by which we live today, are implied in this experience of the "father of believers". Abraham is aware of an "Alliance" between God and himself. This idea of an alliance might be called God's main preoccupation. He wishes to make an alliance with Abraham, with his people and with all the families of the earth. Creation is an undertaking on his part for attaching to himself beings worthy of his love, and attaching them with so close an intimacy that the conjugal alliance alone can give even a faint picture of it. This alliance moreover manifests God's unmerited generosity in an act of absolute freedom. It

is "grace", if we give the word its proper meaning: that which
is entirely gratuitous, springing from God's absolute initiative.
Man nevertheless remains free; God waits upon his consent;
his confidence in God, his "faith", is necessary. God stands
at the entrance to Abraham's tent and solicits a man's hospitality. All God's generosity would remain powerless before his
creature's refusal, for he never takes away his liberty. Abraham
understood, and relied upon God; he staked his life on God's
"promise". He was ready to obey God, however paradoxical
his orders might be: "Go out from your country . . ."; however
improbable they might be: "Take your only begotten son,
whom you love, Isaac . . . and offer him as a holocaust". We
must be ready to sacrifice everything to God, and God will
give it back to us, transformed. The son whom God had given
him, now more his own than ever, Abraham hands over to
God's keeping, and this action has transformed his fatherhood.
God can now carry out his design upon Abraham's posterity,
not merely perpetuating it but establishing the true faith upon
it, making it the people of God. For there is no individual
vocation, however high, which can be conceived of apart from
the community. All experience of God is at the same time a
"mission". (It is impossible to avoid a suggestion of irreverence
in passing over such subjects in a few lines. The reader must
excuse it, realizing that there are inexhaustible riches in these
pages of the Bible which our poor phrases can barely hint at,
and that in the compass of so small a volume nothing more
can be done.)

The Alliance promised to Abraham and to his seed is to be
realized concretely and, as it were, materialized and organized
with Moses (thirteenth century). Abraham had already understood—to put it in modern language—that God is absolutely
transcendent, "the God of heaven, the most high who created
the sky and the earth", and at the same time that he intervenes in history. Moses realizes much more clearly both this
transcendence and this intervention. God reveals to him his
mysterious name "Jahveh", that is, "He is", God says "I am

what I am" in his transcendent and incomprehensible mystery, but also "I am he who is, he who makes to exist, he who controls and animates everything". And God manifests himself in practice as "the Saviour", bringing his people with a strong hand and outstretched arm out of the captivity of Egypt, the Paschal God, who "passes over" with his almighty power and makes his people "pass over" from servitude to the promised land. God manifests himself as the lawgiver of this people. And with this people, which is henceforth for him a people apart, a "holy people", "his" people, a "people of kings and priests", God solemnly contracts the Alliance and dwells in his tent in the midst of his people.

This stage of the Exodus enriches us in its turn with religious values which are essential and definitive: the God of Sinai is the holy God, the Wholly Other, the Transcendent, but he is also God-with-us, God living among us, God communicating his sanctity to men.

God is "the faithful and merciful". But man, alas, is often unfaithful. The sacred history of God's people is the almost unbroken record of its infidelities and of God's chastisement and forgiveness. We shall fix our attention on certain men who have best perceived something of God through the events of this history. We call them the "prophets", a word from the Greek meaning those who "speak for, or in the name of" God. Abraham and Moses were themselves, in this sense, prophets. But the name is more usually reserved for the great inspired leaders of Israel who, from the ninth century to the fourth, were the religious geniuses of a people lacking in genius, people like Joan of Arc and Dante, directly inspired by God.

Previous in time to those who are given the special name of "major prophets", but yet already worthy to rank with them, David, King of Israel in the tenth century, must be recalled. With him God's Promise and Alliance are made much more precise and, as it were, "incarnated". David is the first great King of Israel. With him Israel takes the form of a "Kingdom", the twelve tribes being gathered together around the holy city of Jerusalem. Henceforth the "Reign of God" will be looked for under the figure of the Kingdom. By that we must understand a new order of things, at once exterior and interior, individual and cosmic, which will be established by a more real Presence of God in the midst of men. In the "Kingdom" God will declare himself in his Lordship, his Holiness and his Mercy. The Kingdom of David, indeed, is only a first sketch or rough draft of this. But with David begins the realization that one of his descendants will establish for ever this reign of justice, of holiness and of mercy. There will be a true David whom the opening of Matthew's Gospel will present in these words: "Jesus the Son of David, the son of Abraham".

Since we cannot run through the course of this sacred history, we must be content to notice a few landmarks shown to us by certain prophecies, but without forgetting that God speaks to us above all by events and that the utterances of the prophets are intelligible only in the context of the facts.

The prophet Amos (eighth century) was only a shepherd, a rough fellow who kept his eyes and ears open, when God seized upon him behind his flock to make him his mouthpiece. This man of the people stigmatizes with a sort of tender violence the corruption of his time and the oppression which the rich and powerful exercise over the poor and weak. This is one of his apostrophes to the women of Samaria:

> Here is a word for you, pampered cattle [sic] that dwell at Samaria, the poor wronging, the friendless folk spurning, and ever crying out upon your husbands, Wine, there! We would drink! Never let me be called holy, the Lord God says, if doom does not overtake you for this, see if you be not trussed on spears, and your children given up to feed the cooking-pan.[1]

The people of Israel waits upon God that justice may be done. It hopes in the justice of God to deliver it from its oppressors, and fears this justice of the Holy God on its own account. The fear of God, understood both as fear of a just

---

[1] Amos 4. 1–2.

punishment and as the realization of our own nothingness in face of the Transcendence of God in his Majesty, is not a "primitive" religious feeling. It is true that a higher stage of religion gives peace in the conviction of God's love, but that presupposes a previous journey by way of fear and the permanence of that fear without which all feeling of God's Transcendence would be evacuated.

All the same it was right and proper that Osee, a contemporary of Amos, should put the emphasis on the love, indeed the tenderness, of God. Osee seems to have undergone terrible trials: his wife betrayed him; he forgave her; a second time she left him and prostituted herself; he redeemed her and gave her back the title of wife. Osee understood that such was the unwearying mercy of God towards his people:

> Come back, Israel, to the Lord thy God;
> it is sin that has caused thy overthrow. . . .
> Everlastingly I will betroth thee to myself,
> favour and redress and mercy of mine thy dowry.[1]

The great prophets are only making explicit those aspects of God's mystery which were implicit in the earliest events of Israel's history: to Abraham and to Moses God appeared as he who promises and he who demands, as he who causes fear and he in whose merciful love man may place all confidence.

Isaias (eighth century), maintaining and at the same time rising above these images of God, puts into a strong light God's sanctity. In the vision which the prophet saw in the Temple of Jerusalem and which he has recorded in lines which form one of the greatest passages in the Bible, a gem of a poem,[2] the divine sanctity is represented by a light which the human eye cannot endure, the shining of God's "glory". But this sanctity of the King of Majesty (*rex tremendae majestatis*), which is at once terrible and fascinating, is also a demand for moral perfection and ultimately the source of this perfection. Using the

[1] Osee 14. 2; 2. 19.
[2] Isaias 6. 1–11.

word "justice" in the biblical sense of "the characteristic of the man who conforms to the divine will" (the sense in which we call a balance "just"), we may say that it is already clear in Isaias that man will be justified by his faith in the God who is both just and himself the justifier.

So worship takes on in Isaias a whole dimension of adoration and contemplation of the personal God. Amos and Osee had violently attacked ceremonial worship which was more like a magical ritualism than true prayer. In the temple of Isaias worship is given to God in spirit and in truth.

One note, however, was lacking in this splendid liturgy. It was to be definitively introduced into religion by an extraordinary person, Jeremias (a century after Isaias), a man who had none of the qualities either of an orator or of a man of action, a Pascal who had been given the duties of a police officer. And on him God imposes the most crushing of missions: that of announcing the ruin of the Temple, of weaning the hopes of Israel from their excessive attachment to the royal house, of breaking the confidence of the Jews in the hope of an earthly reward and of criticizing the Law itself. His life was a tissue of failures and sufferings, and he turned against God with a boldness which is on the verge of blasphemous impiety: "he made Jahveh appear at the bar of a tribunal which was his own bruised heart"[1]:

> Lord, thou hast sent me on a fool's errand; if I played a fool's part, a strength greater than mine overmastered me; morn to night, what a laughing-stock I am, every man's nay-word.[2]

With Jeremias, two doors are opened. God is the God of man's heart, the God who knows each man by his name, with all that he is, all that he feels and all that he suffers. And man finds the greatest consolation in the bitterest grief, because in suffering he has found God who, out of death, brings life.[3]

[1] Steinmann, *Le Prophète Jérémie* (Paris, 1952).
[2] Jeremias 20. 7.
[3] Cf. L. Bouyer, *La Bible et l'Evangile*, p. 87.

With Jeremias, with Ezechiel and Deutero-Isaias (Isaias 40–55 and 60–2), with a good many psalms of this period or of later centuries, the idea appears that the lowly and the humble are God's favourites; that self-satisfaction is the worst obstacle to God's entrance into the soul; that the recognition of one's unworthiness and poverty is, on the other hand, the right disposition for giving God a welcome. Gradually we are preparing for the Sermon on the Mount, which Jesus opens with the words:

> Blessed are the poor in spirit
> The Kingdom of heaven is theirs.

Was it right to touch so hastily on these religious attitudes or rather the revelations of God which bring about these attitudes? To refer in a few lines to hundreds of pages of the Old Testament is almost sacrilege. However, since my purpose is to show in what way one can encounter the living God and believe in him, it was impossible not to mention such great witnesses of God as Abraham, Moses, Isaias or Jeremias and not to sum up what they perceived of the living God who disclosed himself to them. The personality and message of Jesus infinitely surpass, of course, these personalities and these revelations of the old Alliance, but the Gospel presupposes them. Anyone who ignores them impoverishes the Gospel dreadfully by reducing it to what it makes explicit and misunderstanding all that (tacitly) it implies. Moreover anyone who has not passed through all the stages of Israel's history, from Abraham to Jesus Christ, with our fathers in the faith, will read the Gospel without grasping the profundity of all Christ's words and deeds. When he hears Jesus speak of the "New Alliance" he will not give the word "Alliance" its full significance, and will not realize that it expresses what is essential in God's design. How, without knowing about the Exodus, could anyone grasp what Jesus means by the enigmatic phrase: "I have desired with a great desire to eat this Passover with you"? And "the soul of the poor", and "justification by faith", and "the dwelling of God among us", and his "glory", and "the people of God", etc., etc. . . . ?

It is none the less true that all these preparations find their fulfilment, and all these figures their reality, in Jesus. Jesus alone is—really—Emmanuel, God-with-us.

I BELIEVE IN JESUS CHRIST

Anyone who reads Paul's letter to the Christians of Philippi must be struck by the continual references to a man well known to the Philippians who seems to fill Paul's whole field of consciousness, a certain Jesus. Paul addresses "the servants of Christ Jesus", "all the saints in Christ Jesus". He cherishes them "all, with the very tenderness of Christ Jesus". He wishes them to be "filled with the justice which Christ Jesus wins for us". For his own part, Paul only lives for this Jesus. Indeed there is much more to it—he only lives by him. One phrase sums it all up: "To live for me is Christ". Clearly Christ realizes for Paul all that the word "live" can express. He is saying:

To live is to be in the light of the truth. Christ is my light.

To live is to be in joy. Christ is my joy.

To live is to triumph over death. Through Christ, I am eternally alive.

To live is to possess oneself, to possess the universe, to possess God. Through Christ I possess both God, and the universe, and myself.

To describe the impression which the letter to the Philippians makes on every reader we should have to speak of a symbiosis between Jesus and Paul. Jesus, then, is not for Paul simply a master to whom one listens, or a model whom one tries to imitate, or even a leader whom one wants to follow. He is someone from whom Paul, here and now, receives life, someone from whom all the faithful, here and now, receive life.

That is what I was trying to express by calling this chapter

"I believe in Jesus Christ". I believe in what he tells me. I put my confidence in him. I stake my life on him. But also and above all, I have my life from him. Jesus Christ "animates" my whole life. And I do not merely receive from him the way, the truth and the life. He *is* for me the way, the truth and the life.

We have here a case which is unique in the history of the world.

Men expect of a master only an instruction or an exhortation or an order. Paul—and with him all Christians—expect of Jesus Life, and the very Life of God. An analogy—and at that a distant one—can be found only, if at all, in the lover who cannot live (so he says) without the beloved, for whom the beloved (so he says) is his whole life.

For Christians Jesus is at one and the same time the motive and the object of our faith: we believe Jesus Christ and we believe in Jesus Christ.

*   *   *

In our debate with the unbeliever—and so in our debate with ourselves, for there is always an unbeliever in us—the one question is this: "Who is Jesus Christ? Who is this man who does not give himself out as an envoy of God, charged with communicating a message, pointing out a way, initiating man into a mystery which is greater than himself . . . but who gives himself out as the one indispensable mediator?" He is not only a channel but the source. He is not only a way, but *the* way. He does communicate life, but is himself the giver of it. He is not only a light in the world, he is the light of the world. Jesus of Nazareth, alone of all men of sound mind known to us in history, makes promises which only God can guarantee, claims for himself what only God can claim.

Either Jesus Christ is the Son of God, God himself, and in that case there is—theoretically at least—no problem. The absurdity would be not to rely on him, not to follow him, not to live by him.

Or Jesus of Nazareth is only a man, a man who seems to be something of a genius and who has been turned into a God. He has a place in history, and we must recognize the especial importance of the part which he has played in the development of a civilization. But he must be "de-mythologized"; his personality must be freed from all that legend, credulity, mystical exaltation or clerical exploitation have attributed to him.

*   *   *

We reject the second horn of this dilemma because it does not correspond with the facts of history. Jesus is not a man whom his disciples have divinized. He is a man who believed himself to be God. Of all men known to history who were sound in mind he is the only one (I repeat, the unique case) who claimed to be God, understanding by this word a supreme, infinite, eternal, omnipotent Being, the Creator and the end of the universe. It is clear that when Oriental kings or Roman emperors had pretensions to divinity they were not claiming anything remotely resembling what Jesus said about himself. Anyone who knows anything about the great founders of religion, Confucius, Lao-Tse, Buddha, Mohammed, is aware that a claim like that made by Jesus Christ never even entered their minds. Mohammed called himself Allah's "prophet". Buddha had received an enlightenment. Confucius and Lao-Tse taught a way of wisdom.

So we must first establish that Jesus did claim to be God, or rather that he was always aware of being identified with the God whom Israel adored. For this end we ought to go through all the Gospels. Since that of St John may appear suspect to unbelievers in view of the relatively late date of its composition (the end of the first century), we shall consider only those of Matthew, Mark and Luke, called the "synoptics" because their accounts can be arranged, for the most part, in parallel columns and looked at all together. What sort of person do they make out Jesus of Nazareth to have been? How did he live and talk?

He has an extraordinary power of attracting men.[1] He hardly begins to speak when vast crowds gather to hear him; if he enters a town, the entire population comes out to meet him; children fall over one another to get near him, and important personages bump into one another in the attempt to bring him their sick. If he retires into the country, people pursue him without bothering to bring provisions with them. On the other hand, he arouses disapproval and hatred from the beginning. All the authorities of the ancient Jewish religion feel themselves menaced both in their belief and in their official position, and vow war to the death against him.

Jesus is as indifferent to enthusiasm as he is to hatred. He makes his own choice of disciples from among those who follow him, and from these again chooses apostles for a special intimacy with him. Over these men, closely attached to his person, he has an absolute mastery, but he does not rely on their help; he never even begins to ask their advice, and he never invites consolation from them. Only once, in his agony, he seems to need their support: "Watch and pray with me", but he wants them to stand by him not for his own sake but for theirs, so that they may find in prayer the power to resist the danger which is imminent: "Watch and pray with me, that you enter not into temptation." Jesus does not depend even on his Mother. He gives no quarter to his adversaries the Scribes and Pharisees. When he speaks to them it is with anger in his face and with his eyes full of fire:

Blind guides who strain at a gnat and swallow a camel. Hypocrites who purify the outside of the cup and platter but are full of robbery and iniquity within.

[1] The notes which follow are inspired by Karl Adam, *The Son of God* (London), esp. Ch. 4.

He drives out the money-changers of the temple with whips, and calls his own King a "fox"....

Yet he never loses self-control for a moment. This fiery fighter never lets himself be carried away. His indignation is always the expression of the highest liberty, that of a man who knows that he has come into the world simply to give witness to the truth. In all his activity he preserves his clear and virile outlook, his harsh sincerity, his impressive loyalty to the cause.

We see in him a man who knows for certain what he wants. From the age of twelve, when he astonishes his parents and the doctors alike by the lucidity of his intelligence and his will, to the hour of his death, we hear him saying continually: "I am come for ...", "I am come only for ...". Not once do we see him, in word or in action, calculating, hesitating, retreating. Could this be imagined? Has there ever been a man of any intelligence who has not admitted, sometime or other, ignorance, hesitation or doubt? Jesus never hesitated for a second. Whenever a question was asked he gave immediately the most luminous and most coherent reply; it is as though he had foreseen everything. He decides his course of action on each occasion without the least shadow of uncertainty; he sees the end clearly; he pursues it without allowing himself to be turned aside by anybody or anything. He is heroism incarnate; he risks his life calmly, freely, deliberately; he goes to death to affirm the truth of the message which he brings; for him it is a matter of course.

*   *   *

But there is something still more prodigious. This "superman", who moves with such independence among other men, whether friends or enemies, who is so conscious of being different from them and of having no need of any of them, has nevertheless loved men tenderly.

But he is no simple-minded enthusiast. He sees all the sinfulness of men. His first words to them are "Do penance!", and he never ceases to suffer from the evil which he sees around him; often he endures the pettiness of his apostles with disgust and repugnance. Yet he never meets a man without loving him. His consideration embraces even those who betray him or nail him to the Cross, and he has a woman's tenderness for any human soul whom he finds writhing impotently in the grip of sin.

He has willed to be poor with the poor, rejected with the rejected, tempted with the tempted, crucified with those who suffer and mourn. He has willed to take on the sufferings of the multitude as his own.

* * *

What, then, is this extraordinary man who is so compassionate towards his brethren, so familiar, so tender, and, at the same time, so independent of everybody, who belongs so entirely to a family, a race and a country ... and who is attached by no human bond? He does not hesitate to abandon his own; in the ruin of his country—which he loves—he sees and accepts the judicial will of "his Father". Much less do riches, honours or even life seem to him to have any value beside "the will of his Father". He is continually alluding to this heavenly Father whom he must obey, whose will directs his life. From the day when, at the age of twelve, he said to his parents "Did you not know that I must be about my Father's business?" to his last words on Calvary, "Father, into your hands I commend my spirit", he has not ceased to put into effect his declaration "my meat is to do the will of him that sent me".

So the key to the life of Jesus will be his submission to a will other than his own, a submission without faltering and without reserve.

Looked at from this angle, the life of Jesus seems even more extraordinary. Admittedly many other men have willed to submit their existence and their actions to the divine will, but there has never been a saint who has not felt all the disparity between his own poor life and the demands of God; people like Francis of Assisi or Teresa of Lisieux have always wept for their shortcomings; much more has the life of a Napoleon or a Caesar been burdened with wrongdoing and remorse; Mohammed and Buddha repented of a great many of their actions. Among all the greatest of our race, only Jesus lived a life without a crisis, without a moral defeat. "This man to whom nothing human was foreign, was yet a stranger to moral evil, compunction and remorse. Jesus exhorted men to repentance, but he did not himself repent. He counselled others to fear, while he loved; to seek, where he had no need to find . . . a unique combination of assured confidence with the most profound sense of religion, of an inborn and tender familiarity that needs no forgiveness on any score with a supremely clear realization of the horror of sin and the demands of justice, of undisturbed security with an infallible sense of what God is and what we are."[1]

*   *   *

But to see the secret of the life of Jesus in his filial submission to the will of his Father would be to stop half-way and to be content with a formula. Jesus comes to preach and to inaugurate the "Kingdom of God", and this Kingdom is a community of life as much with himself as with the Father:

> This is eternal life that men should know you, the one true God and him whom you have sent, Jesus Christ (John 18. 3),

and from the beginning to the end of his life Jesus acts and speaks as though he were one with God. We see him putting himself on God's level on every page of the Gospel; he con-

[1] P. de Grandmaison, *Jesus Christ* (London), II, pp. 209–10.

siders himself superior to all the prophets and all the Kings
of Israel and to the angels themselves. He demands (let us try
to make real to ourselves these exorbitant pretensions) that
we should love him more than father and mother and give up
our own lives for him.[1] He pardons, by his own authority,
offences committed against God. He forgives Mary Magdalen
her sins because of the love which she has for himself. He gives
himself out as the Redeemer and the Saviour, the light of the
world and the bread of eternal life. Finally he will judge all
men on the last day, and will judge them by their behaviour
to himself. . . .

The pretensions of Jesus do not stop even there. He is not
content to put himself on a level with God; he declares that
he is not distinct from God, that he is one with God. He does
not act in the name of any powers which God has conferred
upon him, but in his own name, by his own right. He reforms
the law of Moses, dictated by God himself, he remits sins, he
performs his miracles, he attributes to himself the passages of
the Old Testament predicting the future actions of God, and
all this on his own authority.

On every page of the Gospel Jesus appears as a man who is
aware that he is essentially one with God. Particular phrases
only express what his whole attitude implicitly affirms:

> All things are given to me by my Father, and no one knows the
> Son except the Father; and no one knows the Father except the
> Son, and those to whom he is pleased to reveal him.[2]

Does history witness, then, to the existence of a man, sound
in mind and body, a normal and properly balanced man, who
claimed to be God's equal, identified with God himself?

I know what someone will say: "All that is legend, or rather
the later dressing up of a historical figure. Just as Buddha was

---

[1] François Mauriac writes in his *Vie de Jésus* (p. 48): "It is their
ignorance which prevents many today from detesting Christ. If they
knew him, they could not endure him."
[2] Matt. 11. 27; Luke 20. 22.

gradually turned into a god, so Jesus of Nazareth was given eventually divine attributes and pretensions."

It is quite natural that this should be the unbeliever's first reaction. So we must go back a stage and try to reach agreement on a matter of principle before establishing the facts scientifically.

This principle is simply that on which all science depends: submission to the facts. Anyone who denied the existence of cosmic rays on the pretext that nothing of the sort had been so far discovered would not deserve the name of scientist. Anyone who denied, *a priori*, without examination, that Jesus could have been anything but a mere man, would not deserve the name of historian. It is for us to prove that Jesus was historically such as we have described him. Such a demonstration would require volumes (which have, in fact, been written).[1] We must be content to refer to the main lines of it.

A. *How do we know Jesus Christ?*

We must answer, by the Gospels. And, in the first place, there is no need to be surprised at the hostile silence of the Jewish writings or the curt comments of Roman writers, who had little interest in the theological quarrels of a people in a distant corner of their Empire. What is the origin of the Gospels? Jesus himself wrote nothing; he was content, according to the custom of the country, to preach and to tell his disciples to preach. The repetition of these oral testimonies resulted in a definite scheme which was eventually committed to writing through the desire to reach wider audiences, and with the precise purpose of preserving the "living and enduring word" of the first witnesses. It seems that the first care was to put into writing the words—the *logia*—of the Master and certain outstanding facts: the preaching of the Baptist, the baptism of Jesus by John, the temptation in the desert, the declarations about the Law, the confession of Peter, the passion and the

[1] See, *How do we know Jesus?* in this series.

resurrection. There was certainly an Aramaic text, pretty close to our Matthew and known by Mark. The latter, a disciple of Peter and—for a time—of Paul, put together an account made up of anecdotes in which a faithful memory mirrors the life of Jesus. The present text of Matthew seems to derive both from the primitive Aramaic text and from the text of Mark. It is a didactic Gospel which is chiefly concerned to list the "sayings" of the Saviour. Finally Luke, more psychological and more methodical, goes over the ground covered by his predecessors in a systematic way.

Two questions arise. Have we the authentic texts of Matthew, Mark and Luke? Do these texts inform us about events and statements of which we can be certain?

The reply to the first question admits of no doubt at all. The antiquity of the manuscripts and the papyri, the multiplicity of versions in various languages and the quotations made by the Fathers, guarantee our texts. The substantial variants affect only a minute part of them. The essential question remains.

B. *What is the historical value of these texts?*

I shall establish their historical value by two arguments which seem to be conclusive.

1. The whole geographical and historical context goes to confirm the historical value of the Gospels. For example, documents have recently brought to light the five porches of the pool of Bethsaida, a number which had previously seemed very queer; the Sermon on the Mount fits in with the country by the lake, while the eschatological discourse is unthinkable anywhere except Jerusalem. The Gospels show a true picture of the whole set-up of Palestine at that time. For example, the way in which the powers of Pilate, Herod and Caiaphas were involved together in the trial of Jesus could not have been reconstituted by an author who had not been familiar with this tangle of religious and political authority about the year 30, for that state of things was radically altered during the state of

disturbance from 44 onwards, and still more so after the great insurrection of 66.

2. But the Gospels are even more "paleontological"—to use Harnack's word—from the spiritual point of view; that is, they describe a state of knowledge and a mentality which belong to a time much earlier than their composition. I must explain this further. It is agreed that the texts which we possess were not finally put together before the year 60 (that is about the limit, 70 being more likely). Now at that date Paul had already written his principal letters which were read in all the churches and in which—almost in every line—he explicitly affirms the divinity of Jesus, taking it for granted that his correspondents were in complete agreement with him about it. If it were admitted that the Gospels were the product of the faith of the first Christian communities how, in such a climate of opinion, could our texts fail to contain any explicit mention of Christ's divinity? Read carefully every phrase in our synoptic Gospels, and you will not find the slightest explicit affirmation of the divinity of Jesus, either from the lips of the Master himself or from the pens of the editors. On the contrary, you will find a good many disconcerting statements like the following: Jesus says "Why do you call me good? Only God is good"; Jesus weeps over the tomb of Lazarus; Jesus complains that his Father has abandoned him; his kinsmen say that he has lost his wits, etc., etc. . . .

Either the writers did not believe that Jesus was God, or, believing this, they did not wish to add anything to the events and statements of which they were the witnesses. However we take it, this is a guarantee of historicity which could not be bettered.

It becomes a certainty when we study in detail the personality of Christ as shown in the Gospels. I do not hesitate to say that it is strictly "unimaginable". Consider, for example, the teaching of Jesus. What is it all about? Jesus speaks of country people, winegrowers and fishermen, dealers in precious stones, farmers and day-labourers, housewives and poor widows. He calls up the picture of the doctor of the law with his long fringes, of the young mother happy to see her new-born son, of the marriage procession in the silence of the night, of the rigorous etiquette at the banquet-table, of the unemployed in the market-place, of the rich landowner who goes to bed hugging himself because his granaries are full. . . . We hear of mills, bushels and candles, vines and harvests, camels and chickens, girdles and walking sticks. . . . And these multifarious details of daily life serve to give the answer to eternal problems. The most familiar images allow Jesus to sweep away, with a prodigious independence and penetration of mind, all the pseudo-culture, the prejudices and the rigid rules of the Pharisees, and to state the highest truths about the human soul in a decisive way. The simplest words have the power to kindle and nourish the flame of religious devotion in the hearts of believers all over the world. Who except Jesus could put such profound teaching in so simple a form?

This is only the least of the Gospel paradoxes. If Jesus had never existed, who could have imagined a man with such high and harsh moral demands and at the same time such tenderness for sinners? Who could have imagined that the same man could condemn a covetous glance at a woman as tantamount to adultery and receive without condemnation a woman taken in the act of adultery? In Jesus we find at the same time the sternest exigency and the greatest possible indulgence; the rigid moralist, who condemns the intention and the very thought of evil, lets himself be called, and in fact is, "the friend of publicans and sinners".

If Jesus had not existed, who could have imagined this combination of an extreme sensibility and a woman's tenderness on the one hand and an absolutely unflagging self-mastery on the other?

Who could have conceived of a leader humble enough to wash the feet of his disciples, while treating God as his equal? Who could have imagined a man mad enough to suppose that he does not need to recognize his infirmity and to beg for pardon in face of that infinite transcendence of God which he himself proclaims?

The mass of men produce by comparison only what is spasmodic, unsightly and puerile.

3. The unbeliever protests: "But the element of the marvellous, the miracles, the resurrection? Surely we are not expected to believe in all that as historical fact?"

We must recognize that the miracles which used to rank as the chief proof for the credibility of Christianity have become the chief obstacle to faith in our time. Here certain serious misunderstandings have to be pointed out. When once it has been grasped that God speaks to us more by events than by words, that Jesus Christ is himself the supreme event and that he came to give us a new birth in a new world, then the miracles, and especially the resurrection, appear as the necessary manifestation of this new world. They are the word of God in acts. They "speak" this new world to us.

I shall explain later how the resurrection of Christ is the central fact of history, a historic fact, the historicity of which can be established, and a trans-historic fact, something which transcends history and provides the key to it.[1] The resurrection of Christ is the climax of all previous history and the starting-point of all the rest of history, the final stage of the cosmos. God's whole purpose was to make himself present to the consciences of men; the whole of biblical history is this gradual spreading of the light, this progressive "epiphany" of God; the resurrection is the climax of this epiphany, the showing of the glory of Jesus "made Christ and Saviour by his rising from the dead", as Peter said in his first sermon after Pentecost. And this resurrection is, further, the starting-point for the history of the new world. The risen Jesus has become the Lord of Life and the Prince of Glory, so as to pour his risen life into us, and to make the whole of humanity enter in course of time into his own resurrection, until the day when the new heaven and the new earth appear. In this perspective all Christ's

[1] See Chapter 9.

miracles are simply signs or pledges of the resurrection of the
flesh and an instruction through actions most consonant with
that new Life of which Jesus is at the same time the herald and
the source.

*   *   *

We may now take up again the central question: "Who is
Jesus of Nazareth?" We cannot rank him with the great of
our race. He is quite different from all really great men. Not
to be aware of one's limitations and one's mistakes is a proof
of infantilism or of folly. Jesus is even more different from all
really religious men. To be religious is to have "the sense of
God", the sense of God's absolute transcendence, to recognize
oneself as a creature entirely dependent on the Creator and
separated from him by an abyss. It is also to know oneself as a
sinner and impure in face of God's absolute sanctity. Jesus is
the only religious man known to history who knows and proclaims the transcendent sanctity of God and nevertheless treats
God as an equal.

Either Jesus was what he claimed to be or else a sufferer
from delusions, a most pitiable figure. We should indeed have
to call him something harsher, a certain kind of fool!

Renan brushed this aside with a peremptory gesture of
disdain. "A fool never succeeds. A disordered mind has never
had any considerable effect upon the course of history."[1]

Jesus, on the other hand, appears clearly enough as a man
sounder in body and mind and better balanced than anyone
else, as a man of most extraordinarily calm and farseeing outlook. If we read over the Gospels, we get the impression of a
supremely healthy man. There is no trace of weakness or of illness. He is up early, and spends the whole of his active life in
the open air, on the roads or in the villages. Travelling light,
he walks hundreds of miles. "His last journey from Jericho to
Jerusalem is rightly pointed to as an astounding feat. Under a

[1] *Vie de Jésus*, p.80.

burning sun, along roads in which there was no shade of any kind, through a desolate rocky waste he had to mount some 3,500 feet in his six hours' climb. And the most astonishing thing is that Jesus was not tired. On that very evening he took part in a feast which Lazarus and his sisters had made ready for him."[1]

In this perfectly organized frame are embodied that extraordinary lucidity of thought and that unshakable strength of will which we have seen illustrated. In truth, if there has been a man who could be taken as the norm of perfect balance, of realism, of clear-sightedness and of disinterestedness, that man is Jesus.

And if that man called himself God's equal, God himself, he must have been what he claimed to be.

Thus both the preaching of Jesus and Paul's attitude, with which this chapter began, become intelligible. Paul said, "For me to live is Christ." And he is echoing the whole teaching of the Master who never ceased preaching about himself. Whereas every other Master teaches a truth and a way distinct from himself, Jesus incessantly gives himself out to be the way, the truth and the life. "Come and follow me, I am the light. I am the light of life. No one comes to the Father but by me. Peter, lovest thou me? ..." I, I, I ... there is no other word in the Gospel. To be a Christian, is to *live* Christ, to become a sharer in the mystery of Christ, to allow one's whole life to be animated by Christ. Sin is putting part of my life in brackets, removing it from the sphere of Christ's animating power or just leaving it outside that sphere. By him, with him and in him, I must become a child of the Father and live as a child of the Father.

We are infinitely far from a mere adherence to a doctrine, a system or a self-sufficient moral code. Christianity is a relationship to a person, an engagement to a person. Certainly it is not a blind engagement. We have our reasons for relying upon Jesus Christ. In staking our lives on Jesus Christ we are not

[1] Adam, *op. cit.*, p. 92.

staking a wager, since we engage ourselves with our eyes open, in certainty. I began this chapter by adducing St Paul; I may end it by taking over the apostle's words *Scio cui credidi*, "I know to whom I have given my faith."

CHAPTER IV

FAITH IS AN ENGAGEMENT

All that has been said in the preceding chapter goes to show that faith is in an order quite different from that of mere adherence to a rational truth. Our faith is not submission to a coercive demonstration, but adherence to a Person on whom we rely. I have underlined, nevertheless, that this reliance is "reasonable, rationally justified", and that, conversely, it would be "unreasonable" to refuse faith in Jesus Christ. In chapter eight I shall return to this subject of the relation between faith and intelligence, but at the moment we must deal with the objection which unbelievers so often make: "Is your faith supported by peremptory arguments or not? If it is, everybody ought to believe, and the fact that many do not believe sufficiently proves that your faith reposes on no communicable certitudes, that it is a subjective option, and therefore arbitrary."

The answer is that there are truths of two sorts.

There are truths which can be called purely objective, because they cannot affect my life in any way. If I read in the paper that some gulf has been explored or that some ancient coin has been discovered, it is unlikely that my own existence will in any way be affected. Only my intelligence is concerned. It is its business to assess the evidence. I do not feel myself "engaged".

But there are other truths which do directly influence my life. Political and economic decisions may turn all my affairs upside down, and to "understand" such measures I may need much disinterestedness or a great sense of justice. If I lack these qualities, I shall call an administrative or governmental decision "stupid", and I shall do all in my power to gainsay it. My life is "pledged" by the consequences which follow from my judgements.

Two principles emerge from these remarks:

1. "He who does the truth comes to the light", says John (3. 21). We have constant experience of that in ordinary life: a man becomes a blacksmith by working in a smithy, learns dancing by practising the steps and mountain-climbing by actual ascents. But that is far truer of throwing oneself open to divine truth. The Word of God is addressed to our intelligence, but that is incapable of grasping it without an engagement of our whole being in the ways of God. Like must be known by like: without a certain conformity of our lives with the will of God, his Truth remains alien to us. That was the case with many who heard Jesus of Nazareth.

2. These ways of God are terribly exigent. We have to do nothing less than stake our lives on God. Various (very inadequate) pictures of this present themselves: trusting oneself on a mountain to a friend who holds the rope, risking one's fortune on an enterprise which will not succeed for several years, or even marrying. The Bible frequently employs the comparison with marriage to symbolize the union of God with his people. To have faith is to stake one's life on God's love, to make God one's centre of gravity instead of oneself. It is not merely to renounce other illusory supports, money, fame, comfort . . . ; it is to renounce oneself. We tremble at the words of Jesus: "If anyone would be my disciple, let him renounce himself, take up his cross and follow me" (Luke 9.23). The expression "Gospel of the Sword" has been used to express this.[1] But the teaching of Jesus is only confirming the whole teaching of the Old Testament. From Abraham to Joan of Arc and Charles de Foucauld, God's summons rings in the same terms: "Depart

[1] P. Doncœur has published a pamphlet with this title in which he has collected all the claims made on us by Jesus, the Word of God sharper than a sword (Heb. 4. 12), L'Evangile du glaive (Paris, 1948).

from your own country, leave it, go forth." To be a believer, to be a Christian, is to allow God to become the master of our lives, to renounce proprietorship over ourselves and our destinies. I have already referred to a passage in the Bible which expresses this better than any treatise, the story of the sacrifice of Isaac (Gen. 22). Isaac is the child of promise twice over; he is the son promised by God to Abraham when his wife was barren, and he is the child by whom alone the promise made to Abraham could be realized: "All the families of the earth shall be blessed in you." And now Jahveh demands the sacrifice of this son: "Take your son, your firstborn, whom you love". Abraham, by his faith, is certain that God will "provide", and because he goes to the limits of sacrifice he becomes a father in a deeper sense than he could have suspected. He makes this son God's property, and this gesture transforms his fatherhood. The patriarch who has found in his faith the power to enter into the designs of God becomes his collaborator and the father of many nations.

The sacrifice of Isaac is much more than a striking image. It is the prefiguration of the death and resurrection of Jesus and so of our death and resurrection since we must travel the way which the Master has travelled.

When we say that the Christian life is an "engagement", we must not give the word the weak sense which it often has when human contracts are concerned. It is an engagement to die with Christ in order to rise with him. Christ's paschal mystery must become ours. Our whole lives must be "paschal". Every sacrament—including marriage—makes us one with Christ's paschal mystery. To receive a sacrament is to offer to God the situation in which we find ourselves so that God may take it over and divinely transform it. And to "offer" is not to keep for oneself, but to cease being a proprietor. To offer one's love, for example, is to allow it to develop in God's way, not in ours. It is not only to accept God's law, but to allow him to animate us. It is to allow God to direct this love by the necessities and events which his Providence makes our masters, but also by the inspiration of his Spirit. There is no Christian faith but that which accepts the Sermon on the Mount and, in the first place, its opening words:

"Blessed are the poor in spirit".

Such an acceptance, one need hardly say, is not a matter of the intelligence alone. All the "grounds of credibility" will be insufficient to a heart which refuses to open. Psichari once said a terrible thing: "Our hearts are impure. All our intellectual incompetence springs from that!" That is why the knowledge of God is the fruit of a moral experience, not of abstract reasoning. If we are to believe, we must enter upon a real experience, an experience of love which, little by little, will bring us light.

CHAPTER V

FAITH IS AN ENCOUNTER

The preceding chapter was called "Faith is an Engagement", but it must be made clear that the initiative in this engagement does not lie with us. We can only reply to God's summons "Come and follow me". You do not become engaged in religion as you do in some human enterprise of which you are the promoter or, as we say, the "creator". To become engaged in Christianity is like letting oneself be guided up a mountain, like accepting instruction from a master. Faith, like the whole Christian life, is an encounter in which God takes and keeps the initiative. We might compare the situation, although of course the analogy is very distant, in which a young man loves a girl and seeks to gain her love. He takes the initiative, controlling the proceedings throughout, but perfectly respecting the girl's freedom. We may even say that the more personality he has, the more the girl will feel attracted by him, as though she were moved to action by him; and yet the more free at the same time must she feel her love to be. The disciple of a really great master has the same feeling of freedom. Whereas a bad teacher makes a slave of his pupil, a great master exercises a sovereign influence while leaving full liberty to the person whom he is forming. How much more then must the transcendent God leave our liberty entirely free while moving it at the same time. There is an obvious contradiction between "moving" and "freedom" on the rational plane, on our intellectual level. But only on ours. It need not exist on a higher level. At ground level a traveller cannot find himself in two valleys at the same time, but an aviator can survey both of them. And if even on the human level we can glimpse the possibility of a co-existence between influence and liberty, why should we consider it impossible for God to "move" us while leaving us free?

Henri Bergson found a magnificent and definitive formula for the Christian life when he spoke of a soul "at the same time acted and 'acted upon' whose liberty coincides with the divine activity" (*Deux sources*, p. 248). But I might suggest altering the order of the words. It would be better to say "the soul acted upon and acting" to emphasize that the initiative always comes from God, as it comes, normally, from the mountain guide, the dancing master, the lover. . . .

Our Protestant brethren, starting with Luther, insist on God's initiative in language which shocks and surprises us:

> We must distinguish between two things in Scripture, precepts and promises. Precepts teach what is good, but they do not give the power to do it. They reveal man to himself, persuading him of his inability to do good and leading him to despair of his own powers. . . . Then the divine promises make their appearance. . . . If you wish to accomplish the Law and conquer covetousness, believe in Jesus Christ in whom are offered to you grace, justice, peace and freedom. . . . Thus the promise gives what the precept demands; it performs what the Law ordains. So the precept and its accomplishment come from God alone.
>
> (*The Book of Christian Liberty*)

How many Catholics would be tempted to see in these words a certain pessimism in regard to human nature consonant neither with the Gospel nor with the tradition of the Church? How thunderstruck they would be to read in the infallible and irreformable decisions of ecumenical Councils affirmations which have the same bearing and are even more categorical, for example:

> If anyone says that the development, or even the beginning or again the inclination to believe. . . are not in us through the gift

of grace ... he must be considered opposed to the apostolic dogmas.

(2nd Council of Orange, can. 5 and 6.)

The Council proceeds to make clear that we cannot study, ask for or seek faith except by the grace of God. But none of this need surprise us if we pay attention to the words of Jesus himself: "No one can come to me, unless the Father draw him" (John 6. 44; cf. 10. 29).

Some will object that, on these terms, faith no longer depends on us and that God gives grace to whom he wills. The answer is that the second statement is correct, but that God wills to give his grace to everyone, willing that all men should be saved (1 Tim. 2. 4); also that the whole Bible affirms, along with God's initiative, man's freedom. God's praise or blame, rewards or punishments, would be meaningless if man had no free choice. But we must then add that without grace our freedom is in bonds, for I then lack the self-mastery, the lucidity and the generosity which are necessary for me to be really free; on the other hand, "determinism" applies only to "things". Evil can promote in man an apparent unification, like a torrent which sweeps away everything in its path, but not the unity which presupposes a higher principle of life, as in living beings. A man may have a tendency to evil, but not a necessity deter-mining him to evil. Our freedom is in bonds, but our freewill remains. Grace is offered to us continually to free our liberty. As St Bernard says: "If our soul is blameworthy, it is because it is free. If it is a slave, it is because it is blameworthy, and so because it is free".[1]

These distinctions may seem subtle, but I think them neces-sary. Without stopping longer over them, let us reach con-clusions of the most practical kind. God, like a guide, a master, a lover ... invites us to follow him, to let ourselves be en-lightened and loved, but he respects our liberty. Never in the Gospels do we see Jesus "violate" a soul. The rich young man

[1] On this subject see the two chapters on freedom in Mouroux, *The Meaning of Man* (London, 1948).

cannot make up his mind to follow him; after the discourse about the bread of life in the synagogue of Capharnaum some of the disciples go away; Judas becomes a traitor . . . Jesus leaves them all free. God wants one thing only: to find hospitality in the hearts of men so that they may live in his love and his joy, but he stands at the door and knocks, waiting for us to open (Apoc. 3. 20). To open the door is to pray. All seeking for God apart from prayer is in principle atheistic. It is an absurd contradiction to set about receiving instruction without listening to it. It is an absurd contradiction to set about offering oneself to love while remaining locked up in one's own egoism. It is madness to expect the sun to come into your room if you keep the blinds closed. Such comparisons could be multiplied. Let us say simply that a meeting of two persons can only be a meeting of two liberties, and that prayer is nothing but the expression of our liberty consenting to God's entry into our lives. To pray is to consent to being animated by Jesus Christ. Sin is putting a part of our lives in brackets, withdrawing it from Christ's animation, and the first sin, the essential sin, is not to pray.

I know well enough what the unbeliever will retort: "Prayer presupposes faith. Otherwise it is a process of auto-suggestion which eventually will, of course, provoke faith. But what sort of faith? A mental disorder due to a suggestible imagination." If it is taken for granted that God does not exist, this objection is valid, at least on the face of it. Only results can decide between the believer and the unbeliever, just as only results can decide between the upholders of a scientific theory and their opponents. Let us suppose that someone casts doubt on the existence of cosmic rays. The expert will set up an apparatus which, if such rays exist, should show certain modifications. He will "pray" these rays to show their existence; and if in fact phenomena appear which could only be due to these rays, no one will talk about rays which exist only through auto-suggestion on the part of the experimenter.

In the next chapter I shall speak of the tangible transformation which the presence of God effects in our lives, and how we can, as it were, verify this presence experimentally. For the moment it must be enough to say something about the language which should be employed in this opening of oneself to God in prayer.

Obviously an unbeliever cannot be expected to utter a prayer which presupposes faith, but it is legitimate to ask from him a "conditional" prayer, like the questions asked by the scientific experimenter. Edward Le Roy suggested this prayer:

> I am nothing, I know nothing except that I am full of wickedness, of need, of uncertainty and of anguish.
> I want the good, even the good which I do not know.
> I aspire to something, and I hope.
> I give myself to the God whose inspiring force I feel in my innermost depths.
> I want the light and I call for it.
> I consent in advance to whatever God may demand of me. . . .

It must be added that the encounter between God and man does not take place once and for all. Man has not to discover a destiny reserved for him by God, something which has only to be copied out from a book where it is already written. Our life is a continual encounter with God, an unending *dialogue* with God, something which we have to invent all the time along with him, "the unpredictable discovery of two conjoined liberties", God's and our own.[1]

The more I take my time from God—as the dancer takes his time from the music—the more I shall be free, drawing on the source of all freedom.

[1] Cf. I Cor. 3. 19. V. *Tresmontant, *Essai sur la pensée hébraïque* (Paris, 1953), pp. 43 f.

CHAPTER VI

RELIGIOUS EXPERIENCE

We have spoken of "engagement" and of prayer as though they were separate realities. As soon as we begin to think of faith and the Christian life as an encounter in love between God and man, an encounter in which God always keeps the initiative, while respecting man's liberty absolutely, then we understand that this encounter cannot take place (and still less the invasion of man by God) apart from a whole way of life which is both engagement and prayer at the same time. So we must continue our exploration in the same direction, but we must go deeper and on a wider front.

The prayer which was formulated at the end of the last chapter implies a whole state of soul, an opening of the soul. Simplifying things rather crudely, we might say that there are two sorts of soul, the open and the closed. There are narrow or "blocked up" people, unable to take an interest in anything except their special lines, their comforts and their cars. To avoid caricature let us leave it at this: that there is a whole category of well-to-do self-satisfied people. The people I mean are more numerous among the wealthy ("all this wretchedness is of no interest to us, because we are rich", said a boy of twenty), but complacency is found in all classes. There are people who are complacent about what they are, and especially about what they possess, whether it is money or intelligence or sensibility. They have the souls of property-owners, and religion itself can protect them—so they suppose—against all risks, including the major risk of encountering the living God: "Vote Catholic against all risks", announced an election poster in

Belgium. And not only in Belgium, unfortunately, and not only in politics. Péguy has branded with burning words these "virtuous" people who cannot be "softened up" by grace because they are covered with a carapace of virtue: "Their hard skin of morality is like a coat of leather."

There are people whom dogmas, rites and moral laws dispense from entering into relationship with the living God. At the very heart of Catholicism, as with Israel of old, the cult of idols can dispense them from the search for the living God. From the cult of money and comfort to Pharisaism, how many idols can shut a man up in a universe of three dimensions, so that he knows nothing of a fourth dimension, where the living God is encountered!

Prayer and religious experience can come to birth only in an "open" soul. Let us try to trace out the phenomenology of such a soul. It is one which has a thirst for happiness—not for pleasure and satisfaction—but happiness. Some define happiness as knowledge, and such people never lose the thirst for knowing. Lyautey defined it as activity. Nobody will reject St Augustine's definition: *Amari et amare*—"To be loved and to love." Anyway it seems impossible to define happiness as satisfaction or as a turning-in on oneself. It cannot be considered except as a relationship to something other than ourselves, a going beyond ourselves. It is significant that Gide in his 1926 preface to *Nourritures Terrestres*, in the very act of recommending to us the most carnal and ambiguous sort of passion, purports to have written a manual of detachment and expectation, to have recommended a continual readiness to be acted upon:

> ... Souls never sufficiently filled with love, with expectation and hope.
> Every creature leads you to God.
> Every creature, when you make it an end, turns you away from God.

To have an open soul is to perceive, beyond all our desires for enjoyment, power, praise and even love, a continual creative claim upon us, a movement of inspiration which urges us always to want something "beyond". To have an open soul is not to admit any limit, any final point; it is to have faith, to have confidence in the significance of that work and that light in which we are engaged by a force within us greater than ourselves.

I am not playing with words in speaking of "faith" in this way. I think that God is at work in the depths of our being; and I believe this in conformity with the Church's most explicit teaching (the texts of the Second Council of Orange, quoted above, will be remembered). I think that the first germ of faith is our awareness of God's summons to our hearts, and I am sure that in entering upon and "living" this experience which will make us "do the truth", we shall come little by little to the light, as St John says.

To have an open soul is not, then, to be content with a vague aspiration or just to cultivate pure desires. It is to enter upon and to "live" an experience, an experience of transcendence and love. It is to conform one's life to the light so far received and, in doing so, to discover further light which will make possible the next day's advance. Certain peaks are not visible until one has reached a first eminence. On a lower level, if I may make so material a comparison, the dynamo of a bicycle does not work and put on the light unless one pedals and, conversely, the light makes progress possible. We must use the light which God gives us in order to love, and we must love in order to have more light.

For light is a function of love. There is no need to be surprised at this, since it is Love itself which we are to know, the supreme Love which is God himself. In this domain more than in any other, there is no knowledge except by connaturality Love can only be learnt by loving. So it is obvious that a man who does not love his brethren whom he sees, cannot, as St John says, love God whom he does not see. But we may also say that true love makes many people servants of God who have not yet actually or explicitly encountered Jesus Christ. I do not mean that it is sufficient to love one's neighbour in order to love God, still less that the Gospel is simply a message of universal brotherhood. The commandment which Jesus calls "the second, like to the first" presupposes the first commandment to love God for his own sake. And God is Somebody. If we are content to be kind to our friend's children and say nothing at all to him, our friendship will lack its essential quality. Far more must God be loved for himself. On the other hand, Jesus has said that whatever we do for the least of his friends he considers as done for himself: *ubi caritas, Deus ibi est.*

*   *   *

Love of one's neighbour, disinterested love, like the love for a God still unknown but yet desired, implies a certain forgetting of oneself, a certain detachment, a certain liberation. "You cannot serve two masters: God and mammon", said Jesus. You cannot be turned inwards to yourself and outwards to others at the same time. An asceticism is at the same time the condition and the consequence of a generous life. It is clear enough that it is such a consequence: all "dedicated" lives which fill us with astonished admiration are lives of men and women who do not "belong" to themselves, still less seek themselves. But conversely this readiness to serve is only to be achieved by shedding encumbrances. Pascal said:

> Strive then to convince yourself, not by piling up proofs, but by lessening your passions,

and Psichari said still more clearly, speaking from experience: "Nothing makes us advance in the spiritual life like living on a handful of rice each day and a little salty water."[1]

We shall end, moreover, by realizing that this liberation from our passions, our sensuality, our egoism, is beyond our own powers. This was Paul's experience: "Praiseworthy intentions are always ready to hand, but I cannot find my way to the performance of them; it is not the good my will prefers, but the evil my will disapproves, that I find myself doing. . . . Pitiable creature that I am, who is to set me free?"[2]

---

[1] *Les voix qui crient dans le désert*, p. 243.
[2] Rom. 7. 18–25.

A man who utters this prayer is not far from saying with the Apostle: "Nothing else than the grace of God, through Jesus Christ our Lord,"[1] for the kingdom of God is near to those who do penance. More precisely, it is already within them, according to the wonderful words which Pascal puts on Christ's lips: "You would not seek me, if you had not already found me", if *I* had not already found you.

What I have called "religious experience" is not only the experience of a need, a desire, a thirst. It is also experience of the satisfaction of that desire, and of the quenching of that thirst. The search for God tends to produce rapid results; and one could quote innumerable testimonies of converts speaking of the fullness of life into which they have entered. Here are some from among so many:

> I was blind and I see.
> I was deaf and I hear.
> I was dead and I am alive.
> I am alive, alive, it is wonderful!

That is not a passing enthusiasm, a momentary intoxication. Ten or twenty years afterwards these converts declare that their certitude, their peace, has only grown:

> It is an important and exceptional fact that one cannot be disappointed by Christianity. I have often, indeed, been disappointed by my own infidelity to my baptismal promises, but God never disappoints us, our faith never disappoints us. What ideal—however elevated and however faithful its adherents—can claim anything like this? God gives back a hundredfold what we give him.

And if we ask converts to explain what they mean by this hundredfold, or if we observe for ourselves the effects of their conversion, what do we find? I must be content to quote a few lines which I know to be perfectly genuine:

> Our professor of philosophy had shut us up, saying: "It is impossible to believe in God if you believe in liberty. To be free is to exercise one's liberty, to put it to the test. How can one

[1] Rom. 7. 18–25.

obey God and be free?" In fact that did seem to me unanswer-
able. Liberty meant for me: Gide, Sartre and Camus.

I saw that all that couldn't be taken seriously. I had to look
elsewhere. But where? ... I asked the people around me. Some
despised problems of that kind. Some were content with an
abstract idea of God. But I had just reached that stage, and
wanted to get beyond it.

Unfortunately there were the Catholics. I often sought help
from my Catholic friends. They despised Pascal, they made fun
of Claudel and they lived on detective stories. ... These people
were my greatest obstacle. It took me three years to make up
my mind to seek God in the Church.

Now I really know where I am, that is, after having learnt all
that I was capable of learning. And the liberty which I sought
so earnestly I now feel in the depths of my being. God has
created me a free being. I am free to love him, free to say "yes"
to him. God does not force me. Never have I felt myself more
free, free to save my soul, free to damn myself. I have become
fully responsible.

I have the joy of understanding, the joy of loving. I feel myself
at home in the world. I no longer have the filthy feeling of being
"unwanted". I feel myself at last committed, and everybody and
everything with me.

How generous God is, who has already answered my feeble
prayer so richly.

No testimony could have more weight than that of Bergson,
who, long before his conversion, had studied the Christian
saints and collected in *Les Deux Sources* the results of his
observations. After showing the rise of consciousness in the
brutes and the climax of this evolution in man, the philosopher
then considers the relevant facts to find out whether this process
of evolution goes forward in man himself. He discovers the
forward movement which he was looking for in the saints:

Let us say that the soul has, from now on, a superabundance of
life. There is an immense drive forward, an irresistible impulse
which pushes it on to enterprises of the greatest magnitude. A
calm exaltation of all its faculties gives it great powers of vision,
and, however feeble it is, it carries out its projects effectively.
Above all it sees things simply, and this simplicity, which is as

striking in its words as in its behaviour, guides it through complexities which it seems not even to have noticed. An inborn knowledge, or rather an acquired innocence, suggests to it at once the suitable move, the decisive action, the final word. Effort, however, remains indispensable, and also endurance and perseverance. But they come of themselves, they develop naturally, in a soul which is both acting and "acted upon", whose liberty coincides with the divine activity.

Each of us can verify these conclusions, by studying St Paul, St Francis of Assisi, St Teresa of Avila . . . but each of us knows some man or some woman who realizes today before our eyes, and to the letter, what Bergson describes.

I end this chapter with a last quotation which, in its simplicity and truthfulness, admits of no answer:

How have you failed to reflect on the strange fact that Christians are the only people who possess joy and to whom their faith never brings disappointment, but on the contrary an ever-growing attachment, interest and wonder? I have often heard people, with a rather superior air, making it a reproach against Christians that the reason for their faith is the joy and consolation which it brings them. But it seems to me that no better justification of it could be found, because that is a fact and not an argument.

The proof of bread is that it nourishes, the proof of wine that it inebriates; the proof of truth is life; and the proof of life is that it makes one live!

These are substantial realities against which no argument has any force.

(Paul Claudel, *Positions et Propositions*, II, p. 136.)

CHAPTER VII

THE MEANING OF
CONTEMPORARY ATHEISM

Religious experience, as outlined in the previous chapter, is a
definite fact, a "substantial reality", as Claudel puts it. But
there is another fact, enormous, pervasive and overwhelming:
atheism is sweeping over our world like a tide. It is as though
humanity, having once reached a certain stage of its development, had to get the religious virus out of its system, whatever
services religion may have rendered it at earlier periods of its
history. It would be childish to approach the problem of faith
today without facing this major problem, which puts a question
mark against everything which has been so far said.

I. *The facts* can be briefly stated. Anyone can verify them for
himself. France is a missionary country where the numbers of
practising Catholics among the working classes is less than two
per cent (when one thinks that, a century ago, the great majority
of the workers were Christian, and that they surrounded the
clergy as they blessed the trees of liberty!). But it is not only
in France that atheism sweeps away the workers. A German
priest, Karl Rahner, writes: "In ten years, unless an unforesee-
able change takes place, Christians, and Catholics most especially, will be like the Hussites or Vaudois or the Dutch Jansenists
in the eighteenth century." Let us look at it still more widely:
almost all coloured students in Paris, from Viet Nam, Japan,
China, India, Africa, Arabia . . . lose the faith of their parents.
They come from Buddhist, Hindu or Mohammedan families,

and they smile if you mention religion to them: "We have something better to do." Man used to be defined as a "religious
animal", and it has been shown that signs of religion have never
failed to appear in any culture from the first traces of civilization down to our own time. But a new fact is now staring us
in the face, radically new but undeniable: it has been given to
the twentieth century to see the emergence of an atheistic
civilization.

It is true that there have always been atheists, especially
among intellectuals, but not only did they not prevent the
generality of men from living religiously, they themselves
behaved as though God existed. Jean-Paul Sartre is still heard
to say: "I am the first logical atheist." Today one cannot dis-
miss atheism with Robespierre's lapidary formula: "atheism is
aristocratic". Atheism is no longer a snobbery of profligates,
anxious not to be mixed up with the common people who
believe. Atheism today is democratic and intellectual at the
same time. God is felt by the people to be an obstacle to progress, and atheism seems to be the condition for the realization
of all human hopes. The masses have assimilated Karl Marx's
principle: "Atheism is humanism achieved by the suppression
of religion."

*   *   *

II. *The origin of modern atheism.* To understand contemporary atheism it would be necessary to trace it to its origins,
and that is not within the scope of this small book. But a few
indications may be given. Faced by the evil which the barbarian
invasion had produced, bishops and monks had to assume the
direction of nearly all profane activities. From these historical
circumstances was born that medieval Christianity in which
the whole of life was built up and developed in the Church and
in the Church's way. The Church was the real context to which
one was conscious of belonging: princes and magistrates, consecrated by the Church, acted (or refused to act) as sons of the
Church. The family, the professions, the university, public
health, peace and war ... all was controlled by the Church as
if it were a part of herself.

This could not last. The emergence of absolute royal power and the birth of nationalism produced a separation of politics from religion. Thought, morality and—with a thinker like Spinoza—religion itself was envisaged more and more as depending on man alone. One could perhaps say that the foundation of the "modern world" goes back to St Thomas, and give him the credit for sounding the death knell of the Middle Ages. For the Angelic Doctor did proclaim the value of created realities, restore their autonomy to profane functions and give the intelligence its proper rights.

Paul Hazard puts the great turning point between 1680 and 1715: "What a contrast! What a sudden change! In the seventeenth century men loved the hierarchy, the discipline, and the public order which authority undertook to ensure, the dogmas which gave life a fixed pattern. The men of the eighteenth century, their immediate successors, detested constraints, authority and dogmas. The former are Christians, the latter anti-Christian. Most Frenchmen thought like Bossuet; suddenly they began to think like Voltaire."[1]

More and more man becomes aware of his own possibilities; his reason can make unlimited progress in the knowledge of the world, and therefore in its utilization and transformation. The invention of the infinitesimal calculus, the discovery of the sources of energy, the continuous improvement of machinery, all these justified man's pretensions and opened up an endless field for his activities.

Religion seemed to the learned an abdication of the intelligence in face of the problems posed by the world around. It appeared to the technician an alienation of man's powers. Certain pictures give forceful expression to this state of mind. In a film of Eisenstein's there is a double picture: during a time of drought, a moujik kisses the earth and the clergy organize processions; while Soviet workers build dams and cut irrigation channels. The official spokesman comments: "For two thousand years the faithful begged their daily bread from God. The

[1] *La Crise de la conscience européenne*, preface, p. 1 (Paris, 1935). English trans., *The European Mind* (London, 1953).

glory of having heard humanity's prayer will soon belong to the Soviet workers."

Nietzsche and Feuerbach had said so long before. Man creates God and alienates himself for the sake of a myth, stripping himself of his own wisdom, his own will, his own justice. "Poor men make a rich God. Religion becomes the vampire of humanity, and nourishes itself on man's substance, on his flesh and blood. The more religious a man is, the less he is a man. It is true that this sort of tension has enabled man to disengage his own consciousness through 'reflexion', but that necessary stage has now been passed, and the turning point of history will be the moment when man becomes aware that man's only God is man himself." The exploding of the myth alone can bring the alienation to an end.[1]

That is how the great masters of the nineteenth century prophesied. And that is how our contemporaries instinctively feel. Behind all modes of thought, there is today—spread through the whole population—an atheistic experience which could be formulated at least to this extent: "We live very well without God", and which is sometimes more positively expressed by saying, "We can only really live without God." Contemporary atheism, then, is not the rejection of this or that religion as apparently valueless. It is the absolute atheism of men who have chosen to stake everything against the divine transcendence and against every trace of transcendence, who have opted for an absolute immanentism. It is a positive, organic, constructive atheism. This faith in man can indeed work in two different directions, but in either case only man's own possibilities are taken into account: there is Promethean humanism, the optimistic and quasi-triumphant humanism of Marx, the man of the nineteenth century; and there is the cynical atheism, disinfected from all illusions, of Merleau-Ponty, Sartre or Bataille, men of the twentieth century.

* * *

III. *Our faith confronted by modern atheism.* I do not think

[1] See H. de Lubac's book, *The Drama of Atheistic Humanism* (London 1953).

that I have minimized facts or attitudes of mind. The Church is going through the greatest crisis in her history. We may be cut to the heart, but we have no doubt about the validity and efficacy of our faith. I shall try to explain myself clearly.

1. *The advantages of modern atheism.* In the first place we should rejoice at all the purifications of religion which have resulted from the evolution sketched above. Particularly we may hope that science will eventually destroy magic, which is the contrary of religion. The religious man has a duty to subject himself to God; the magician believes that he can subject God to himself. If ever the moujik shown by the Soviet film thought that he could subject God to himself by magical rites, we can only rejoice at the destruction of this belief in magic. May science free us from all mythological explanations and all magic rites! Whatever science may discover, it is just that which we refuse to call God, for the first cause cannot be reduced to the status of the second cause.

Let us also rejoice that man is reaching his adult stage; an over-clericalized world would be too rudimentary and infantile to meet the Spirit's embrace. In medieval Christianity the mastery of the spiritual over the temporal had been gained prematurely and with too great ease. The clergy's control of all profane activities stifled to some extent the initiative of lay-men and overlooked secondary causes. Everything in the world is subject to the royalty of Christ, but it is not desirable that everything should be subjected to clerical control. "Render to Caesar the things that are Caesar's."[1]

Once upon a time the Church relied upon profane institutions under clerical control to form Christians and to keep them in God's service. It seems much more in conformity with the Gospel and shows greater respect for the freedom of faith when the Church forms Christians by her own proper means, preaching and the sacraments, and then sends them out into the world to be the leaven in the mass. But we do not wish to envisage that problem here except from the angle of faith.

[1] This requires lengthy development. See Yves Congar, O.P., *Lay People in the Church* (London, 1957).

2. *Faith and the modern mind.* If the present evolution of man favours in the long run the purification of faith, it is not surprising that this purification should involve risks, and that the pride of twentieth-century man should produce—at least for the time being—a certain number of difficulties which must now be considered.

A scientific mentality pervades our world and will increasingly do so. More even among the masses than among the learned, only what has been documented, proved, tested, is held to be true. Thus the data of faith seem not to fall under the normal criterion of truth. Dogmatic facts such as the Trinity, the Creation, Christ's Resurrection, belong to a sphere inaccessible to the human reason. If people believe in them, it can only be for irrational motives, therefore, by some leap into the unknown. Faith can be only a subjective and incommunicable option.

I cannot accept such suggestions. Let me explain myself by a comparison. Suppose I am travelling and am struck down by a serious illness while staying in a village. I look at the possibilities of consulting a competent doctor. I conduct the inquiry as fully as I can and put myself in a doctor's hands only after finding reasons for complete confidence in him. At this point my ignorance of medical questions obliges me to give up my active part in the business, at least to some extent. I obey the doctor by undergoing the treatment which he prescribes, but I remain the judge of the effects which the treatment produces in me, and a cure will be my best reason for having faith, henceforward, in the man who has cured me. Let us leave that stage aside, for the moment, and concentrate on the first one, the preliminary inquiry. Our faith is not blind. It rests upon a historical inquiry. We are familiar with a series of events, from Abraham to Jesus Christ, which reveal God to us. Our critical judgement has free scope for a scientific study of these historical facts. At this point certain of our contemporaries will protest that truth can be attained only by scientific reasoning and experiment. But we must repudiate this vice of the modern mind and maintain that there are historical certainties. The evidence of witnesses can produce a certainty as rigorous as any other means of knowledge. Everyday life would be impossible if we doubted this.

What must be repudiated in this so-called scientific mentality is a narrowness of mind which refuses to break its bounds. I shall return to this central point.

Some of our contemporaries, those who profess the disillusioned and de-theologized humanism alluded to above, do not accept the clarity of God's purpose as manifested throughout history. In the name of honest doubt faced by the unknown and of intellectual courage, they refuse "belief" as an easy option. A clear-minded man, they say, must be content with reality, however sombre. Jean Rostand's pamphlet *Ce que je crois* will be remembered in this connection.

Here I must protest against a double misunderstanding. In the first place lucidity consists in seeing the light wherever it happens to be. I cannot call lucidity a refusal to recognize that a lamp illuminates its surroundings. If Jesus Christ had never existed or if Jesus of Nazareth is only a man, well and good. But this must be proved to me. If, on the other hand, I can show that Jesus Christ reveals God to me, it will not be lucidity, sincerity or courage to deny this light. Behind the attitudes of men like Camus, Malraux or Thierry-Maulnier, the same *a priori* principle can be detected which I was pointing out in connection with a certain scientific mentality: the refusal to admit any truth which transcends men, the refusal of a "revelation" from outside. In each case faith comes up against an "immanentism" which is—by definition—incompatible with it. Faith is the encounter with the living God, the confident laying open of oneself to the living God. Any refusal by man to go beyond himself and to accept God is irreconcilable with faith. Courage, sincerity and lucidity must consist, on the contrary, in accepting the great adventure on which God wishes us to embark.

For—and this is the second misunderstanding—it must require a very thorough ignorance of Christianity to suppose that it offers men an easy and comfortable solution! God's first intervention in human history begins with the order given to Abraham: "Go forth from your country, your family and the house of your father ...". And the same order continues to echo throughout the history of Israel, the Gospel and the history of the Church. Prophets, apostles and saints will be invited to leave everything and to start on the adventure. The man who is self-satisfied and self-confident is the man whom Christ casts out of his mouth. Dostoievsky's cry is only too true: "O Christ, you have come to turn us upside down!" When God bursts into a human life, he turns upside down the existing order, and brings, not peace, but a sword.

As Gabriel Marcel has said in a definitive phrase: "To put one's centre of gravity in God, and not in oneself—apart from that there is no religion." The first condition of faith is to accept a dependence, to enter into an order which one has not—of oneself—invented. But man has a terrible fear of "losing his life".

Man rejects God today in the name of progress, of humanity's onward march. There must be no talk about "losing his life"; he is conscious, on the other hand, of a duty to possess it to the full. Humanity has seen its means of knowing and utilizing the world increase for centuries. Man's needs could only grow in the same measure. Humanity has been launched upon an ever-quickening forward movement, and has become aware of the necessity and the value of this forward movement.

The notion of evolution has been imposed on man today to the extent that he cannot in practice perceive any living being otherwise than as engaged in a spatio-temporal series. As Père Teilhard de Chardin says[1]: "What makes a man 'modern' and classifies him as such (in the sense in which a whole crowd of our contemporaries is not yet modern) is to have become capable of seeing not only in Space, not only in Time, but in Duration ... and that is to be incapable of seeing anything otherwise—anything—starting with oneself." Man discovers that he is the

[1] *Le Phénomène humain* (Paris, 1955), pp. 242–4.

axis and the spearhead of evolution, that he is nothing but evolution become conscious of itself. To see in humanity today only the rise of nationalism among people who have been kept in dependence for centuries, or a fever of scientific discovery or an effort of productivity, would be to perceive only accidental manifestations and to overlook the deep-seated movement which animates them. Humanity is henceforth and definitively aware not only of its possibilities for transforming the face of the earth, but also of its power to transform itself and to perceive in itself the forward movement which began with the light of the first stars.

Now it is in the name of this forward movement—whether it be called the liberation of the oppressed, or scientific research or productivity or anything else—that humanity sees in religion today a dangerous alienation. There is no graver conflict, just as there is no more mistaken one. It is the whole possibility of faith for man today that is at stake. If religion seems to him opposed—or even indifferent—to this forward movement which sweeps him on and with which he wants to collaborate with all his powers, then it can only seem to him an absurd aliena- tion, the projection into a metaphysical heaven of a living force of which the life of the planet is unjustly robbed. The whole question, then, is whether there is opposition or convergence between the Christian faith and this faith of man in himself and in evolution. We must reply without hesitation that the God whom so many of our contemporaries reject, the God whose existence is supposed to impair the dignity of the universe and to cut at the root of human endeavour, is a "pseudo-God", and not the living God.

Oriental beliefs (a subject to which I shall return) may con- ceive of spiritual development as a negation or condemnation of the "phenomenon", but the Christian faith loves the crea- tion which is in travail until it shares in the glorious liberty of the sons of God (Rom. 8. 19–22). The whole Bible, from the first chapter of Genesis to the last chapter of the Apocalypse, shows us a universe which God has formed with his own hands and which he has entrusted to man, a universe in which man is summoned to work with God. This forward movement is not meant to stop at the insertion of God's Son into our world by his Incarnation and the introduction of Christ's Body as the leaven in the mass. The exact contrary is true. We Christians have no fear of being divided between a faith in the World and faith in God. The one is unthinkable without the other.

The realization of the "Pleroma", the fullness of Christ's Body, requires the achievement by our world of the natural term of its evolutionary development. And, on the other hand, it requires that all those who have faith in man must see that all their efforts will remain ineffective and dehumanizing so long as they reject the dimension of transcendence. If only they could understand Karl Jaspers' thought: "There is no existence except by reference to transcendence".

We cannot end this chapter better than by giving two quotations from Père Teilhard de Chardin[1]:

"For nearly all ancient religions, the renewal of cosmic views which characterizes 'the modern mind', has been a crisis from which they will never recover, if they are not already dead. Closely bound up with untenable myths or involved in a passive and pessimistic mysticism, they cannot adjust themselves to the precise immensities or the constructive demands of Space-Time. They cannot fit into the conditions of our Science or our Action."

On the other hand, "if the World is a convergent system and Christ occupies its centre . . . man finds himself capable of discovering God and subjecting himself to God throughout the whole length, width and depth of the World in movement. . . . Christianity represents the only current of thought bold enough and progressive enough to embrace the World practically and effectively. This alone can lead us not only to serve but also to love the redoubtable movement which carries us forward."

[1] *Le Phénomène humain*, pp. 330–1.

CHAPTER VIII

FAITH AND INTELLIGENCE

Our reflections on contemporary atheism will give us a better grasp of the relations between faith and intelligence. We realize that we have much more than "reasons for believing". The rational justification which allows our intelligence to be a consenting witness of our faith is the perfect homogeneity of our beliefs and their correspondence with reality. And there is no other "proof" of any truth in the scientific field. The truth is that by which one understands the greatest number of realities, and as Chesterton profoundly said: "A truth is not true when something demonstrates it, but when everything demonstrates it." Increasingly every day I am struck by this perfect harmony between my faith and all realities, human and cosmic, and by the complete coherence of all the aspects of my faith.

Such an experience is hard to communicate by reason of its very range. One can only pick out certain particular view-points.

A well-known capital at Vézelay has been called "the mystical mill". There are two people on either side of a handmill. On one side Moses pours into the funnel the grain of the Old Alliance; on the other St Paul looks with astonished eyes at the flour of the New Alliance. The mill symbolizes Christ. The richness of this image gives scope for endless meditation. For all the realities which we meet in the Old Testament find their full realization in Christ. He is—in the fullness of their meaning—the Temple, the Sabbath, the Law, the Vine, the People

of God, the Manna, the living Water of the desert, the Passover, the Paschal Lamb, the Prophet, the Priest, the King, the
Alliance, the Word of God. . . . It is a question of realities, not
of poetical artifices. You need only study a biblical lexicon
with attention to become aware of these identities which could
not have been realized by mere accident.[1] The New Alliance is
indeed, as Bossuet said, "Jesus expanded and communicated",
like a homogeneous flour which gives us Christ whole and
entire.

Moreover each of the realities which I have brought to mind
—and many others—embraces the whole sweep of the divine
economy. Let us take an example. God promises Abraham an
heir and an inheritance. The objects of the divine promise are
immediate realities: the heir is to be Isaac, the son of Sara who
was previously sterile and already advanced in years; the inheritance is to be the land of Canaan. But the subject of the
divine promise is also the whole race of Isaac down to Jesus,
the son of Abraham (Matt. 1. 1) and ourselves, who are heirs
of God and joint heirs with Christ, called to share the inheritance of the saints in light (Col. 1. 12). This inheritance is the
land of promise which was in the first place Palestine, but
became little by little the "Kingdom", that is to say a new order
of things, both inward and cosmic, in which God's sovereignty
is exercised in holiness and mercy. That is the land promised
by the Beatitude: "Blessed are the meek, for they shall possess
the Land."

Let us take another example. Genesis (1. 26) tells us that
God made man in his own image and likeness, and that he
placed him on earth to be his representative. But only Jesus
is the perfect Image of the Father, by whom God has been
revealed to us (John 14. 9). One day we shall at last see God
face to face (1 Cor. 13. 12), and then "we shall be like him, for
we shall see him as he is" (1 John 3. 2).

These are tiny examples, not at all convincing in them-

[1] For example, we shall explain briefly in Chapter IX, p. 77, that
Jesus is the true Temple.

selves. But for anyone who reads the Bible with sufficient care, the continuity of the themes, the closely woven texture which they form, the light which the first page sheds upon the last, and conversely, produce an unshakable certainty.

The same experience can be repeated with each of the mysteries of our faith. The sacramental economy, which seems so astonishing to so many unbelievers (and even to Christians) may be taken as an example. There can be relations between persons only through signs—actions, gestures or speech. God could enter into relations with men only through these signs, more precisely by actions accompanied by speech. First of all there were all the events of the Old Testament: the vocation of Abraham, the release from the captivity of Egypt, etc. The great sacrament was Jesus, the efficacious sign of the relation between man and God. All our sacraments are efficacious signs by which we are assured of a personal encounter between Christ and ourselves, by which Christ takes the situation which we offer him and gives it a divine consistency and reality.[1]

But it is impossible to put in a few lines a fact which produces certainty only by a grasp of its universality: nothing in our religion can be detached from the totality of our belief; whatever question may be raised, I cannot answer it without having recourse to Jesus Christ in the context of the whole Bible and in union with the Father and the Holy Spirit. Christianity is a living being each organ of which is in dependence on the whole body and at its service. That is certainly the difference between a living being and a corpse. Life is recognized by the total interdependence of all the parts of the living thing. To Taine's proud declaration about his state of mind at the age of fifteen: "I had too high a regard for my reason to believe in any authority but its own", I should like to oppose the witness of Jacques Rivière: "I have become a Christian in order to understand."[2] St Augustine had said this in three words: *crede ut intelligas*. Accept the mystery and all will become clear.

[1] On this subject see Roguet's excellent little book, *The Sacraments, Signs of Life* (London, 1954).
[2] *De la foi*, pp. 37–46.

The central mystery of our faith (I am tempted to say, the only mystery), the only one which the Church requires a catechumen to profess with solemnity, is the mystery of the Trinity. How can so many people call themselves Christians and think of this mystery only as an abstract and sterile formula? The Bible has taught us that man was created in God's image. It is not, then, absurd to think of God in our image, provided that we apply our concepts to him only analogically, respecting his complete transcendence. Each of us recognizes in himself a subject whose principal actions are thinking and loving: I think, I love. Jesus has revealed to us that in God there is a source of infinite being, an absolute starting-point, a *plenitudo fontalis*, whom he has taught us to call the Father, and of whom he has said that he is all love. This Father utters an eternal Word by which he is eternally expressed and who realizes all his love: his well-beloved Son who *is* all his love. And we see this Son in the Gospel wholly turned towards the Father, a movement towards the Father and nothing else. Finally Jesus speaks to us of the Spirit whom the Father and he himself will send, who proceeds both from the one and from the other, who is the Breath of love and, as it were, the living kiss of the Father and the Son. So the very being of God is constituted by this exchange in which there is "You" and "I" but no yours or mine. None of the divine Persons has anything which he keeps to himself, of which he is the proprietor; all that the Father has belongs to the Son and the Spirit—and it is the same with the other Persons. Absolute Being is at the same time absolute Love, and we understand that it is the degree of "openness" that a being has which determines the degree of his personality.

But at the same time the whole of creation is illuminated by this light. It now appears as an enterprise of generosity and —so to say—an overflowing of the Trinity beyond itself. Creation has taken place as an enhancement of the Son. The world has been made by him, for him and in him. God has made the world to be a sort of vesture for his Son: *Christus amictus mundo*. He has predestined us, before the creation of the world, to be his well-loved sons in his own Son (Eph. 1. 3–6; Col. 1. 15–17). If we had a total view of the universe, past, present and future, we should see all the lines of the universe, all the generating forces of the universe, converging upon a meeting-point which gives them consistency and intelligibility. And this central point is Jesus Christ, the Father's only Son who has been introduced into the world to "affiliate" it, to communicate to it his own divine filiation.[1]

That, very roughly sketched out, is the synthesis to which I referred. I am persuaded that a correct account of the Christian mystery would be enough to provide certainty of the truth of our faith to any "open" intelligence, just as it is the horrible caricatures of this mystery which make so many reject a belief known to them only as a hotch-potch of more or less incoherent affirmations. It is not a question of demonstrating the Christian faith but of "monstrating" it, of pointing to it as one points to the light. The faith is luminous in itself and spreads light throughout the world.

[1] I shall return to this consideration at the end of Chapter XI.

CHAPTER IX

THE RESURRECTION OF JESUS, THE CENTRE OF OUR FAITH

Our whole faith is objectless if Jesus has not risen. This language will perhaps surprise Christians themselves. Yet it is the apostle Paul's declaration:

> If Christ has not risen, your faith is a delusion; our preaching is groundless, and your faith is groundless (1 Cor. 15. 14, 17).

We must take these words quite literally. I know that the resurrection from the dead seems impossible to men of today, at least as much as to the Athenians who refused to listen to Paul any longer when he uttered the word "resurrection". But we cannot compromise about this fact or even leave it provisionally in the shade. The resurrection of Jesus is not a supplementary miracle to confirm our faith, or an obstacle to our faith to be whittled down. It is the very centre and object of our faith. We have every reason to believe that the first confession of Christian faith involved simply the two lines of St Paul's letter to the Romans:

> Thou canst find salvation, if thou wilt use thy lips to confess that Jesus is the Lord, and thy heart to believe that God has raised him up from the dead (10.9).

We must also notice that the two affirmations are equivalent.

In the language of the New Testament the Lord is the risen Jesus; Jesus has become "Lord" by his resurrection.[1]

*   *   *

Before "showing" that the resurrection of Christ is the centre of our faith it should be established that this resurrection is a certain historical fact, one of the best attested facts of history. But the small size of this book makes that task impossible. I must refer the reader to the books which do perform it.[2] But I would just point out that the disciples' conviction about the resurrection of their Master is not a consequence but a cause. It is not the end of a process, a doctrinal elaboration or a later legend. It is the initial impulse, the first outburst of Christian life. For between the life of Jesus, ended by his death, and the birth of Christianity there is a gap. The religious movement brought into being by Jesus ended with the apparent failure of his death, an apparently absolute failure since what he preached and offered as the Way, the Truth and the Life was simply himself. If Jesus himself is to be adored as alive, a triumph of life must take place to compensate for the failure of death. A new experience must occur strong enough to compensate for that of Jesus' death. The disciples must have had the experience of his *return to life*. We can pretend that this experience was only subjective, but we must at least admit that such an experience could not set in train a religious movement unless it affected a number of minds. The death of Jesus, at the great assembly of the Jewish Pasch, had been a spectacular public event. An individual's visions could not cancel the shattering effect of this. And if several minds underwent the same experience, or rather different but converging experiences, is there not ground for supposing an objective event at the source of this experience? Lastly

[1] E.g. Acts 2. 36: "God has made Lord this Jesus whom you have crucified" (cf. Acts 4. 10). Cf. the words of Jesus himself (Matt. 26. 64; 28. 18), and also Phil. 2. 9–11; and the whole Apocalypse which is at the same time the gospel of his "Lordship" (1. 5, 12, 18; 5).

[2] See Bibliography at the end of this book.

isn't it much more difficult to explain the rise of Christianity without the fact of the resurrection than to admit the fact itself?

Now we have testimonies to this fact, the course of which we can easily trace, from the first discourses of St Peter, preserved in their bare and almost simple-minded formulation (Acts 2. 22–36; 3. 12–26; 10. 33–43), down to the detailed accounts of the evangelists, by way of the first liturgical hymns and the first profession of faith preserved in St Paul's letters.[1] The study of the texts of the evangelists is particularly interesting. It shows the development of the testimonies. The text of Mark (16. 1–8) is primitive, abrupt and summary. It mentions only the empty tomb and the awe and consternation of the women. Matthew (28. 1–20) insists on the futility of the guards and the sealing of the tomb, and makes the mountain on which Christ appears a new Sinai whence the Saviour casts his light upon the nations of the world and upon history. Luke (24. 1–53 and. Acts 1) makes the resurrection "assimilable"; that is, it is linked up with the pattern of history and with the psychology of the witnesses. As contrasted with the visions of mystics, which are parentheses in the life of the subject, prodigious distractions, ecstasies, the appearances of the risen Christ occur during a walk along a road, a visit to an inn, a meal in a house, and these actions of everyday life pursue their course the while. Whereas Matthew speaks only of an appearance in Galilee, in Luke Jerusalem becomes the geographical turning-point as the resurrection is the historical turning-point. Finally John (20–21) has preserved—as a privileged spiritual observer—a whole series of facts which were not transmitted in the tradition which Mark, Matthew and Luke summed up and stylized. Everything becomes at the same time more historical and more theological—more historical because the facts put together in a fragmentary way by Mark, Matthew and Luke are organized into a coherent account in the discovery of the empty tomb, the

---

[1] 1 Cor. 16. 22 (this very primitive Aramaic invocation presupposes a living Saviour). 1 Tim. 3. 16. Ephes. 5. 14. Rom. 10. 9. 1 Cor. 15. 3–5.

appearances at Jerusalem and the doubts of the apostles, the appearance in Galilee and the commissioning of the apostles; more theological because in the course of the Fourth Gospel the *passion* and the *glory* are intertwined. Just as Jesus in his passion gave life and was already triumphing in glory, so after his resurrection he keeps the marks of his passion.[1]

A later editor ends the Gospel of Mark by a further summing up of the facts (Mark 16. 9–20).

Such apparently divergent texts illustrate, if anything does, Heraclitus's principle: "An implicit agreement is more valuable than an explicit one." The deep-seated harmony of these different testimonies has great weight.

*   *   *

The greatest difficulty, then, does not lie in these divergencies between the testimonies. It lies in the strange nature of the appearances of the risen Christ. Far from passing over this difficulty in silence, I am not afraid to underline it, for the very strangeness of the appearances is the clue to the significance of the resurrection.

We must notice first of all the hesitations of the witnesses when they meet the risen Jesus. The disciples do not recognize their Master at once. Mary Magdalen takes him for the gardener; two disciples travel with him and talk with him at length without recognizing him; Thomas refuses to believe until he has touched his wounds; Peter does not recognize him on the lake-shore, and doubts seem to be betrayed even by the evangelist's declaration:

"None of the disciples dared to ask him 'who are you?', for they knew well that it was the Lord" (John 21. 12).

Moreover Jesus himself admits this difficulty about recognizing him since he tries to convince them by explaining the Scriptures, by eating, by making the disciples touch him.

[1] On the combination "death-glory" in the Gospel of John, see 2. 18; 3. 14; 6. 51; 10. 17 and especially 12. 23–41; 13. 31; 17. 1.

What, then, are we to say about Jesus' risen state if those who lived with him for several years could not immediately recognize him? He is certainly the same Jesus with whom they had lived: gentle, considerate, tender, the friend of holy women; but also firm, severe, even sometimes harsh. He remains the leader, the master of the future, the law-giver of the Church (each appearance carries with it an investiture). He remains the friend of all, but still has special affections. Some of his characteristics reappear, such as his way of breaking bread and especially his way of teaching and his significant miracles (the miraculous draught of fishes).

However, the apostles' hesitation is enough to suggest to us that Jesus is no longer just the same. In fact you have only to bring the texts together to realize the differences—for example, about Mary Magdalen, John 20. 1–2 and 11–18 on the one hand and Luke 7. 35–50 and John 19. 25 on the other.[1] In the two words exchanged between Jesus and Mary Magdalen: "Mary" —"My Master", all the past is gathered up, while the following words: "Touch me not, for I have not yet ascended to the Father," introduce us to a new form of existence.

It is the same if we compare John 21. 15–19 and Matt. 16. 13–23 (or Luke 22. 34–62). We knew the good-hearted Peter, ardent, loyal, generous, speaking a little too hastily, but accepting rebuke, sometimes also weak. . . . We find again the same Peter, but now very humble, before the risen Jesus. The past remains intact. But it is taken up, transfigured and brought to its conclusion. Everything becomes sacred in the statements now made by Jesus, with their warnings of sacrifices to come and their promises.

To take another example, Jesus had often to rebuke the incomprehension of his apostles: "Have you no sense, no wits, even now? Is your heart still dull?" (Mark 8. 17). The same incomprehension requires the same correction on the day of the Ascension, but the tone is different: "It is not for you to know the times and the seasons which the Father has

[1] On this subject see Guardini, *The Lord* (London, 1956), p. 417.

fixed by his own authority but you are to be my witnesses"
(Acts 1. 6–7).

Compare too Jesus when bound by his mortal flesh to the
race of David, who devotes himself only to the "sheep of the
house of Israel" and sends his apostles only to them, with the
risen Jesus who commands his followers to make disciples of
"all nations".[1]

Who, then, is this risen Jesus, so identical with what he was
before his passion and yet so different? The Christ of the
appearances is not the mortal Jesus living again, in the way
in which the risen Lazarus takes up again his former existence.
Jesus appears and disappears, enters the Cenacle while the
doors are shut. Nor is the Christ of the appearances an immortal Christ still hampered by the bonds of this world. On
the contrary he is the Christ who has been "raised up with the
Father", glorified with the Father, established as Son of God
in the majesty of power (Rom. 1. 4), born to a new life, and
who is trying to initiate men into this "fourth dimension" of
the world. Here we touch the heart of the mystery.

The resurrection of Jesus is a historical event of a unique
kind. It is certainly an event in the world's history. Jean
Guitton proposes the word *en-stasy* as opposed to ecstasy to
indicate the character of the risen Christ's appearances. The
ecstatic is a man who is drawn away from the realities of this
world by a mysterious force. Visions are parentheses in their
lives for ecstatics; they are for the time being "distracted" from
this world, released from it. The appearances of the risen Jesus,
on the other hand, are inserted into the texture of everyday
events: a journey along the roads, a fishing expedition, a meal.
The apostles can say: "We ate and drank in his company after
his rising from the dead" (Acts 10. 41). But the resurrection
of Jesus is an event which does not come from this world. We
could call it a *trans-event*, a *trans-reality*.

And that is why these appearances, which give the disciples

[1] Matt. 10. 5; 15. 24; 28. 19.

so vivid an impression of reality, nevertheless seem clearly to presuppose faith, at least a partial faith which they are to develop and transform. The resurrection presents itself to us as an experience and a hope at the same time, as the link which binds history to another sort of existence. Imagine a perfectly polished sphere on which are moving tiny little animals, quite flattened out. They would recognize only two dimensions. If a pin were inserted into the sphere, they would suddenly have the strange and almost incomprehensible revelation of a third dimension. They would have the same sensation if a being like themselves suddenly detached itself from the surface of the sphere. To return from this geometrical picture to the reality which it is trying to explain, everything suggests that the risen Jesus wished to introduce his disciples to the experience of a fourth dimension in our world. He lived with them for forty days in the attempt to make them understand that eternity was now germinating in time, but that its true home was elsewhere.[1]

We now begin to perceive why the resurrection is the centre of our faith. The risen Jesus is the first-born from among the dead (Col. 1. 18; Apoc. 1. 15), the first-born of all the new creation (Col. 1. 15), the germinal cell of the new world and the figure of it in its final form, the Alpha and the Omega (Apoc. 1. 8; 21. 6; 22. 13). Jesus is the second Adam, the true Adam (1 Cor. 15. 45 and Rom. 5. 12–21).

So the resurrection of Jesus teaches us in the first place that our bodies will rise one day in glory, since we are members of the risen Christ (1 Cor. 15. 12–17). And as our bodies are bound up with the whole cosmos there is a "dimension of expectation" in the entire creation. We may notice in passing that this is the significance of the miracles, especially those of healing. They are anticipations or figures of the resurrection of the flesh. They are, as it were, the first streak of that dawn when souls and bodies too will be saved, so as to live for God. They are words of God, echoes of the great proclamation of Jesus

[1] Read on this subject Guardini's *The Lord* (London, 1956), the chapter entitled "Between time and eternity" (p. 416).

resurrection whereby the Lord announces to us the new creation.

The resurrection of Jesus is thus at the centre of our faith because it completes the revelation of God, who has been try-ing, since the time of Abraham, to make himself known to us. It is the supreme "Epiphany", for in the risen Jesus we have seen the "Glory" of God, as John says (1. 14; 15. 5). But at the same time we have the pledge and the first realization of the final state to which humanity and with it the whole creation must attain.

*   *   *

But the resurrection of Christ has not only this eschatological value: it is not only an anticipation of the glorious final state of creation. It is also a source of life here and now. As St Paul has admirably explained, Christ has been made by his resurrec-tion Lord of the World. This Lordship has been given to him as Head of the Church which is his body, the fullness of him who fills all in all, the perfection of him who is in every way perfect (Ephes. 1. 19–23; cf. Col. 1. 18–19). A unique work of art can bring us more quickly than any explanation to the heart of this mystery: the tympanum of the entrance to the basilica of Vézelay. An immense Christ in majesty, with arms open wide, is enthroned in the heavenly Jerusalem. His serene face is that of the immutable and eternal God. His outstretched hand is the right hand of the Almighty. His human foot has trodden our earth, but his robe and mantle seem to be caught in a great gust, in a whirlwind which emanates from himself. The light of the Spirit plays upon the Saviour's hands, and the great gale of Pentecost makes the robes of the twelve apostles, much smaller than their Lord and Master, billow and swirl. Around the apostles, and through their means, the whole of creation is being stirred by the breath of the Spirit: men of all trades, farmers, fishermen, soldiers ... all races from giants to pygmies, all the signs of the Zodiac, every created thing,

The Christ of Easter is he who sends his Spirit to recreate the entire universe.

To show still more clearly the central position of Christ's resurrection in the economy of our salvation I would recall two further texts from the fourth Gospel. When Jesus drove the merchants from the Temple, the Jews asked him for a sign to justify the mission which he claimed for himself. He answered them: "Destroy this temple and in three days I shall raise it up" (John 2. 19). It is hard to show in a few lines all that is implied in these words. Christ in the flesh is, as it were, the keystone of the old Temple and of the old economy. Through his mortal flesh, Jesus, son of David, son of Abraham (Matt. 1. 1), belongs to the ancient Israel. He considers himself sent only to the lost sheep of the house of Israel (Matt. 15. 24), but after the resurrection he is to reign over all nations (Matt. 28. 19–20). By putting him to death the Jews destroy their own Temple, since he is the keystone of it; and the risen Jesus becomes the new Temple. The body of the risen Christ replaces the building made with hands, and there is no longer any form of worship for us but that which gives us a share in the mystery of Christ's death and resurrection.

Another saying of his is no less significant. It was uttered at the feast of Tabernacles, the most joyful and most popular of the Jewish feasts. In the midst of the crowd waving palm leaves, a priest escorted by Levites went down to the pool of Siloë to draw water in a golden ewer. The procession then returned to the Temple, and the trumpets sounded three times while the priest performed the solemn sprinkling of the water. This water recalled that which had sprung up in the desert during the Exodus, and it foreshadowed the marvellous water which Christ would cause to spring up[1] and the river of water which Ezechiel had seen flowing from the new Temple of the messianic age.[2] The national feast of water gained a still greater solemnity on the seventh and last day of the festivities. And it

[1] Isaias 12. 3; 44. 3ff.; 49. 10.
[2] Ezech. 47. 1–12.

was on this day that Jesus cried out: "If anyone is thirsty, let him come to me. And let him who believes in me drink. As the Scripture says, rivers of living water shall flow from the breast of the Messias" (John 7. 37–8). Henceforth it is from the body of Christ that the faithful will draw the water of the Spirit. The risen Christ will pour out the Spirit over the whole earth. How clear the sculpture of the tympanum at Vézelay now appears to us!

Let us follow up this discovery. Christ's risen and glorified body is, as it were, the Church's mother earth. Before his resurrection Jesus was, in his corporeal nature, only the living being of a son of Adam. By his resurrection he has been transformed into life-giving Spirit.[1] The body of Jesus has risen as a mystical body. But this adjective "mystical" must not mislead us. The Church is the Saviour's physical body. It is Christ himself existing corporeally. Our union with Christ is not merely a union between members of a society, as in Aesop's fable of the body and its members. Like all Jewish thought, which unites body and soul, body and person, inseparably, St Paul's thought is more realistic than this. To belong to the body of Christ and to belong to Christ is one and the same thing. We are concorporate with the risen Christ. The sacraments of the Church, especially baptism and the eucharist, incorporate us with the risen Christ, make us become the physical body of the risen Christ. We are the people of the risen Christ. Certainly this life is still hidden in us. "What we shall be has not yet been manifested. We know that when he appears we shall be like him, for we shall see him as he is."[2] The risen life which we already possess will break forth in glory.

So it is no exaggeration to say that the resurrection of Christ is the centre of our faith; we could almost call it the unique object of our faith. We believe in the resurrection of Jesus, seeing in it the first fruits of this new and eternal creation which is the outcome of God's plan for the world, and understanding

[1] *"The Lord is the Spirit"* (2 Cor. 3. 17).
[2] 1 John 3. 2.

that the whole of human history has as its purpose the gradual transference of the substance of the first Adam into the substance of the New Adam, the risen Christ.

There lies the whole mystery of that Church of which only the human face, the too human face, is seen by unbelievers. There is the dazzling mystery of that Church which, alas, seems only to hide God from so many souls who seek him.

CHAPTER X

FAITH IN THE CHURCH

Faith was defined earlier in this book as a personal encounter with the living God, and nothing would ever persuade me to go back on that definition. I could never admit that there may be any interposition—whether of a person or of a thing—between the living God and ourselves. I feel in perfect agreement with my Protestant brethren in declaring with St Paul that Christ Jesus is "the only mediator" between God and man. Yet it appears that I cannot go to God, encounter God, both in principle and as a matter of fact, except by the mediation of men. This is very obvious in the Catholic Church, in which the priest gives the sacraments, the bishops and the popes define the faith and the hierarchy governs. But our Protestant brethren themselves, from the beginning of the Reformation, and increasingly in our own times, have also maintained that we cannot go to God without our brethren. They like to quote Calvin's words: "It is impossible to be born to the life from above, save in the womb of this mother (the Church)", words which are very much like those of St Cyprian: "No one can have God for his Father, unless he has the Church for his mother". How can we reconcile this necessary mediation of a Church with the immediate contact with God in which true "religion" (*religare*, to bind) consists?

The solution of this problem would require a whole volume. But we cannot brush it aside for a double reason: the Church is the means of faith and the object of faith. It is impossible to answer the question: "What is faith?" without pointing out that faith must be defined, to some extent at least, in terms of the Church; to believe is to put one's trust in the Church, because only through her can I find Jesus; to believe is to adhere to the dogmas which the Church infallibly proposes for my belief; to believe is to encounter God continually in the Church and through her. I need not insist that this is the chief point of difficulty for our contemporaries. They may be willing to admit God's existence; they may even acknowledge Christ's function; but, precisely because of God's transcendence and Christ's sanctity, they are unwilling to see in a human church —too human indeed, involved in the pettinesses of politics and the miseries of sin—the way, the truth and the life of God. Faith in the Church, faithfulness to the Church, is the most controversial aspect of the faith at the present time. But it is not for us to decide whether the Church is useful or not. The answer to the problem must be sought from God: what has he willed and what does he now will? The sacred history of salvation answers on every page: God has not ceased to will that men chosen by him shall teach their brethren his ways. What were Abraham, Moses, David, the prophets . . . but "mediators" through whom God has made himself known and has revealed his ways to men? And if it is objected that Jesus Christ has "perfected" mediation to such a degree that any other than his own is henceforth unthinkable, I need only open the Gospel to find Jesus giving to the twelve (or to his disciples) a mission like that which the Father has conferred upon himself: "As the Father has sent me, I also send you. He who hears you, hears me. He who despises you, despises me. I am the light of the world; you are the light of the world. God alone has the power to remit sins; know that the Son of God has the power to remit sins; sins shall be remitted, for those for whom you remit them. . . ." Why multiply quotations? Everyone remembers them, and you have only to open the Gospel to find them everywhere. In regard particularly to faith, there is St Paul's quite definite statement: *Fides ex auditu* . . . Faith springs from preaching, and preaching takes place at Christ's bidding (Rom. 10. 17).

In fact God respects this principle, and he, the Almighty, has such a regard and love for us that his activity is conditioned by our cooperation. Even the apparent exceptions do not fall entirely outside this economy: Paul was stricken directly by God's hand on the road to Damascus, but Christ sent him to Ananias for instruction. In any case how can we be surprised, since it is God's purpose to gather us together in the unity of love, that a bond of brotherhood in our search for God should be the beginning and the test for our final communion in heaven? Indeed it is a glorious thing that God should will this "sacrament of our neighbour" as the means by which we learn of his own Love.

Since the scope of this book prevents us from going any further into this problem, we shall pass directly to our main subject: *faith can be found only in an experience of the Church*. What is the meaning of "an experience of the Church"? Contact with a person or persons through whom we meet the Church, the body of Christ, and, therefore, Christ himself. This experience can be very limited, yet exhaustive. A single authentic Christian may be enough to reveal God to a soul which is seeking for him (just as, unfortunately, a bad Christian is too often the barrier which turns souls away from Jesus Christ for ever). I choose, from among many, two opposite testimonies:

> I have often sought help from my Catholic friends. They have been my greatest obstacle.

And this, in which one might substitute "Catholic" for "priest", for what is said of this priest should apply to any Catholic:

> I remember the first time I was getting ready—at the age of twenty-three—to see a priest, the very first time I had met a priest alone so that I could consider him, listen to him and talk to him. I had the notion that I was going to see someone who lived by God and with him. That is what a priest was for me, a man living by God. I told myself that this must prove to be so, or the whole thing must be a fraud.
>
> You priests do not understand that we judge you in this way, by this almost external witness of God which you give us. A priest's faith must go out from him. He must show God. We

must be able to see that he lives by God. Then God, who was "impossible" for the atheist, becomes "possible". You cannot fail to be struck, disturbed, overcome, by a priest who is really a witness of God. You cannot pardon one for not being so in some degree.[1]

To repeat, read these lines with "Catholic" substituted for "priest", and you realize the nature of the question put to Catholics by unbelievers. They are not much interested in the details of what we say to them. What they want to discover is the presence or absence of a relationship to God. They want to see whether we are "indwelt" by God. If they find only a doctrine, a system, principles (!), they turn away disappointed, perhaps for ever. But if an unbeliever finds a Catholic in whom he perceives the mystery of a Presence, faith becomes possible for him.

What has just been said of the individual Catholic has far greater force in the case of a Catholic community. As with the individual Catholic, the influence may work either way. The "Catholic world", too often bound up with a certain political attitude, is the greatest obstacle to the evangelization of the modern world, and in particular of the working class. Here there is a great and dreadful responsibility to be faced. The Church, which unbelievers do not distinguish (and how should they?) from the "Catholic World", instead of being the standard set up above the nations and proclaiming Christ, is the screen which hides the Saviour from sight. Conversely a group of Catholics living a family life in prayer and charity produces an extraordinary impression on unbelievers. When a community is formed on a genuinely evangelical basis, even if its activities are of the most ordinary kind, the witness which it gives to God as he lives and works within it is practically irresistible. The Church's great hope today lies in these local or professional or educational communities, based upon prayer and the liturgical sacrifice, and offering a welcome to all souls of good will.

---

[1] Quoted in *Qu'attendez-vous du prêtre?* (Paris, 1949), p. 221.

On a higher level we find a still more effective and impressive witness in communities of men and women who are consecrated to the Lord. It is impossible to spend a few hours in, say, a Trappist monastery without being struck by the life which these men lead, and even by the beauty of their faces and the clearness of their eyes. It is impossible to meet the Little Sisters of Père de Foucauld without being amazed by the life of these girls who, from Korea to the Andes, from Morocco to the country of the Eskimos, from the leprous villages of darkest Africa to the tents of the Iraki nomads, share the most wretched and despised conditions of life, in order to extend Christ's incarnation and to bear witness—simply by being there and by sharing the sufferings of others—to the love and joy of our well-beloved brother and Lord, Jesus Christ.

Consider too the witness presented to unbelievers by the annual students' pilgrimage to Chartres, or by the faith and patience of the sick at Lourdes. Apart, then, from so much that is distressing about the Church, there are many ways in which she can be discovered in her authentic purity. But she is known in her divine reality only by those who are not content to remain "spectators" but take an active part in her life. What was said earlier about the necessity of prayer and action for finding God applies here also. A man must himself enter upon what I have called "an experience of the Church", that is, he must unite his personal prayer to that of the community and *do* the truth, here also, so as to come to the light. What is necessary for the discovery of the faith remains necessary, too, for its preservation and its growth. It seems impossible—especially in the conditions in which we live—to make our faith grow unless we belong to a Christian community of suitable size (ten to thirty persons) so that we can hope for the support of our brethren's progress, the inspiration of their devotion, fraternal correction and—in some cases—encouragement to heroism. The parish community ought to be the community of these little communities, and through the parish and the diocese our "communion" must be, finally, with the Church herself. Can we find the God who wishes us to be one in love without sharing in this communion and without putting our trust in this Church which is the body of Christ?

For the Church is also the object of faith: *credo Ecclesiam*. Not that the Church is distinct from Christ as a sort of mediator in addition to him—as Protestants suppose us to believe! In Joan of Arc's words: "Jesus and the Church, it is all one".

The cables which transmit the electric current from the power station are not a fresh source of the current; their function is to communicate it, not to create it. The Church, in Bossuet's phrase, is nothing but "Jesus spread abroad and communicated".

* * *

That is why we believe that the Church has received from Christ the mission of transmitting to us the Word of God and of interpreting it infallibly. A Christian who was asked about the content of his faith once replied: "What do I believe? Ask that of Rome." Such a reply—if it does not cover up ignorance or apathy—is a legitimate one. We do expect from the Church the definite and unquestionable transmission of the Revelation which God has made to us. But it is understandable that this simple answer produces a host of problems for unbelievers, as for Protestants and for Catholics themselves. We shall touch on them in so far as it is necessary to answer the question "What is faith?" and so also the question "What truths do we believe?"

The content of our faith can be only what God has revealed to us both in the Old Alliance and in Jesus Christ. He has not handed out to us a series of propositions; he has instructed us by events, and in the end he has given us his Son Jesus Christ and his Holy Spirit together with a system of means by which our life "in Christ" is brought into being and sustained. These means cannot be considered apart from the action of the Holy Spirit in the community and in each one of us. They are a sort of body, a sort of sacrament, in which the Holy Spirit, the soul of the "tradition", is at work. Faith is part of this tradition which gives the Church its framework, but it is not a dead deposit—it lives in the Church. This life of revelation is divided into two periods. In the Old Testament, during the earthly life of Jesus and the lives of the apostles, revelation has grown to its completion. With the death of the last of the apostles it has been completed. The episcopal body has the task of preserving the apostolic word, of proposing it for our belief and inter-preting it. "Tradition" is now "the doctrine entrusted (*tradita*) to Christ's Bride, the Church, to be preserved and infallibly interpreted".[1] But—let me repeat—this doctrine is not preserved in the Church as the metric standard was preserved at the Pavillon de Breteuil in Sèvres. We are speaking of a witness which is eternally alive in the Church, a witness animated and guaranteed by the Holy Spirit.

Our Protestant brethren are scandalized at the idea that we can believe in the infallibility of the Roman *magisterium* or that of the Councils. That seems to them far more pretentious than a claim by the Society of the Friends of Pascal to give an infallible interpretation of the *Pensées* or the *Opuscles*. In this case it would be a matter—after all—only of human thought; but for the ecclesiastical hierarchy to claim an infallible inter-pretation of God's thought! That would indeed be monstrous if the Church were only a human society. But it is quite a differ-ent matter if God himself continually speaks to us in the Church, rather as Jesus Christ is continuously present in the Eucharist. Now there is a double activity of the Holy Spirit in the Church. On the one hand, the apostles and their suc-cessors have received an assurance from Christ that the Holy Spirit will be in them so that they may teach without error.[2] On the other hand, the Holy Spirit assists the faithful so that they may adhere to God with a faith which is truly living, the formulation of it being provided by the Church's hierarchy. The apostolic college (and, in the midst of it, the Bishop of Rome playing the part of final criterion of unity and orthodoxy) is assisted by the Holy Spirit to teach infallibly. The faithful are assisted by the Holy Spirit to believe infallibly.

[1] "*Fideliter custodienda et infallibiliter declaranda*", says the Vatican Council. Sess. III, cap. 4.
[2] E.g. Matt. 16. 18; 28. 16–20; Luke 10. 16; 22. 32.

We may now look again at the words quoted above: "Ask Rome what I believe." It is quite correct in regard to the objective determinations of belief, which hierarchical authority controls. But it would be incorrect if it suggested that the faithful have only to believe "passively". To believe is no doubt to listen in the first place; but it is also to adhere in heart and soul, to commit oneself, to think and to act. St John tells us that he who believes in eternal life has the witness of God in himself.[1] The hierarchy has authority to impose formulas, but it is the part of the faithful to think and to develop this datum.

When we speak of the Church's infallibility in matters of belief we must always bear in mind these two forms of the Church's life: the Church as an *institution* which has for its mission to give the Church its framework, and in particular to preserve and interpret her belief, and the Church as a *communion* which lives this belief infallibly, but without forgetting for a moment that these are two aspects of one and the same Church, the body of Christ, animated by the Holy Spirit.

It is no part of my task to state the content of our belief, or even to show the limits within which this belief is infallibly defined. I shall merely say that the doctrinal decisions of the Pope or of ecumenical councils (that is to say, of the body of all the assembled bishops) are quite infrequent. Teaching is normally given in more ordinary ways, and the assurance of infallibility then consists simply in the fact that the whole Church will never accept a doctrine contrary to the faith.

I may now return to the question put at the beginning of this chapter: "What relation is there between our faith in Christ and our faith in the Church?" I reply:

1. Our faith in the Church is inseparable from our faith in Christ. We cannot put our trust in Christ and refuse to put this trust in his orders and in his work. Moreover we do not consider the Church as distinct from Christ; we see in her his body: "All of us form but one body in Christ, the very body of Christ".[2]

[1] John 3. 15, 36; 5. 24; 6. 47. 1 John 5. 10.
[2] Rom. 12. 5; 1 Cor. 12. 27; Eph. 1. 23; cf. 1 Cor. 10. 17; 12. 13; Eph. 4. 16; 5. 30; Col. 1. 24, etc.

This identity between faith in the Church and faith in Christ is particularly clear in baptism, which is often called the sacrament of faith. A previous faith is required of a man who desires baptism. At one time the first question put to the candidate was, "What do you ask from the Church of God?", and the candidate answered "Faith". He was then entrusted to Christians who instructed him for three years. During the Lent which preceded his baptism, the bishop questioned the catechumen and eventually asked him to make a solemn profession of his faith. He could receive baptism only on this condition.[1] But, you will say, what is the good of baptism if faith was there before it and it is faith that "justifies" us and makes us conformable to the divine will? I answer that the sacrament is bound up with faith; that the faith which justifies carries with it the desire for baptism, since Jesus himself has said: "He who believes and is baptized will be saved" (Mark 16. 16). It would be impossible to emphasize the inseparability of faith and baptism more clearly, and this remark leads us still further.

2. It is through the Church that we go to Christ. Adhesion to the Church is not a result of having already obtained salvation, but this adhesion to the Church itself "justifies" us. The Church is a mother in the strictest sense; it is from her that we receive life. It is not in the first place through literary documents, dead in themselves, that I have known Christ, but by the living witness of his Church. And it is by baptism that I have been incorporated into the Church, and so into Christ. Baptism is the sacrament of spiritual regeneration by juridical and mystical incorporation in the Church. Entering into the Church comes first.

The inseparability of the Church and Christ is the reason why the Christians of China are suffering and dying at this moment. The persecution is aiming precisely at a divorce between loyalty to the Church and loyalty to Jesus Christ, by stirring up a movement for "autonomy" against the "foreigner". The words of Fr John Tung Shih-chih must be remembered: "A movement which has no connection with the hierarchy is inviting us today

---

[1] Note that we find this already in Acts 8. 37.

to attack the Pope's representative. Tomorrow it will ask us to attack the Pope, the representative of Jesus Christ. Why should it not ask us the day after tomorrow to attack our Lord and our God . . . ? God, the Pope, and the Pope's representative are all one!" At the moment when these distinctions, legitimate in theory, threaten to break up the homogeneity of the mystery of Christ and his Church, Catholic China has found its motto in these words of the Fr Tung—a rocklike fidelity to the Church's hierarchy.[1]

*   *   *

With these thoughts in mind we can understand the traditional formula: "Outside the Church there is no salvation".

But this statement raises terrible difficulties: are all those who do not belong to the visible Church excluded from salvation? Has not each religion the same pretensions, and is not the multiplicity of those religions itself a proof of the futility of such exclusive pretensions? All that has been so far worked out seems to be back in the melting pot again, and it is imperative to find a solution for these problems.

[1] See J. Lefeuvre's admirable book, *Les Enfants dans la ville*, a record of Christian life in Shanghai from 1949 to 1955 (Paris, 1956).

CHAPTER XI

THE OBJECTION BASED ON THE MULTIPLICITY OF RELIGIONS

It seems impossible to avoid the following dilemma. Either all religions are only different ways of moving towards God, adapted to various cultures, mentalities and periods of time, and in this case the best is that which is the best adapted to the circumstances in question. Then the universalist claims of the Catholic religion are baseless, and even more so its claim to be the one true religion. As Simone Weil wrote: "In fact, the mystics of nearly all religious traditions are practically identical".[1] Or else the Catholic religion is what it claims to be, the sole ark of salvation. But in this case how can the persistence of so many other religions be explained, and what becomes of those who do not know anything about Christianity, or reject it?

I shall put my reply in the form of a parable. On a certain planet was a mountain whose peak towered up into the sky. Men were always dreaming of reaching its summit. Expeditions were undertaken by all races, each attacking the mountain with its own special resources and on that side of it which faced them. Sooner or later each party came to a stop, supplies failing and the air becoming unbreathable. But one of these

[1] *Lettre à un religieux*, p. 49. (Eng. trans., *Letter to a Priest*.)

parties—one of the least well-equipped—found itself suddenly and mysteriously reinforced with supplies and respirators. Moreover shouts from above guided their further progress. The members of this party were now, as it were, "worked" by a transcendent force, and all they had to do was to bring their freewill into line with this supernatural activity.

To translate the parable: up to the appearance of the Judaeo-Christian religion, Simon Weil's statement is more or less sound—all mysticism is an effort, adapted to a certain culture, by which men strive to reach God. But what I want to make clear is precisely that Christianity—as opposed to all these human efforts—is an initiative on God's part to which men are only asked to reply by their faith. Thus Christianity is something quite different from a mere moment in the religious evolution of humanity. It is not a transient stage between the more primitive forms of religion of the past and the more developed forms yet to come—still less is it a form of religion destined to pass away with the disappearance of all religious "alienation".

Nor can Christianity be reduced to a "spiritual existence" for which dogmas are as inessential as are the words of a particular language to express a reality which would be formulated just as well in another language.

Still less again would we accept the pragmatism of some of our contemporaries who desiderate a combination of "spiritual" forces to combat a materialism which they find alarming.

I want rather to bring home to the reader the transcendence of Christianity by showing him what it really is and by confronting it objectively with the great religious or atheistic movements which divide our world today.

*   *   *

Let us first remember that Judaeo-Christianity[1] is the only "historical" religion, that is, that God has revealed himself by events and in particular by the event of Jesus Christ, culminating in the resurrection. We believe that God has broken into

[1] See above, Chapter II.

human history by intervening in the life of Abraham, by calling and guiding Israel. We believe that he has made himself present to us in Jesus Christ, and that he is always at work in history by his Spirit. Christianity is nothing but a "Sacred History", the movement of history animated by God and advancing towards the Parousia.

What a contrast with the religions of the Far East! For them history has no part to play. Moreover history belongs to the world of appearance and illusion from which we must free ourselves. Time, like the world, is only a mirage, the realm of *Maya*. The mystic's effort must be to free his soul from everything contingent and illusory so that he may become one with the universal soul and plunge himself into the undifferentiated Absolute.

But the historical character of the Christian faith, and of this alone, is no less clear when we compare Christianity with the other religions which have issued from biblical revelation: Judaism and Islamism, which have lost this knowledge of God as the master of history. Judaism, which has been entirely built up by the revelation of God through the events of Israel's history, has become gradually fixed in a static fidelity to the Law of Moses. And Islam sees in Abraham, Jesus or Mohammed nothing but reformers whose task was to re-establish monotheism in its primitive purity.

Christianity is thus the only religion for which God's plan is realized in the development of a sacred history. But this peculiarity leads to a still more fundamental originality and transcendence. A Christian does not look for salvation from an effort the control of which, or at any rate the initiation of which, is in his own keeping.[1] He can only put himself in the

---

[1] Many Christians, Protestants and Catholics alike, will be surprised to read these words of a Council proclaiming an infallible truth in which we must believe: "Reward is due to any good work which we do, not by reason of any merits whatever which preceded grace; but grace, which is not due, precedes good works so that they may be done" (2nd Council of Orange, can. 18).

hands of God who alone can enable him to pass over the double gulf which stands in his way; first the infinite gulf between the creature and the creator, between our participated being and the transcendence of the inaccessible God, the Wholly Other; but also the gulf between the Sanctity of God and the sin which holds us captive. We believe that God—without any merit on our part and while we are still sinners—calls us freely to share his own divinity, demanding only our humility and our faith.

The opposition with Buddhism, for example, is patent. The attraction of Buddhism for certain Westerners lies in the possibility which it claims to offer of uniting oneself with the eternal without having to commit oneself to an Other and submitting oneself to him. The category of the divine is no longer the exclusive property of a personal and infinite Being. It is a domain into which man can penetrate through his own initiative, relying only on his own resources. To be a Christian, on the other hand, is to permit the bursting in of someone upon our own lives, God upon history, to believe in the bursting in of God upon history, to believe that God is unceasingly at work in each of our lives, to consent to God in faith. "The Gospel is the power of God for every man who believes" (Rom. 1. 16).

In the end there is only one question to answer: is this alleged intervention of God's a fact? I shall not repeat the account given in Chapter II. I shall only insist that the decisive criterion is the person of Jesus himself. Jesus of Nazareth, who always put himself on a level with God, is either a poor deluded visionary or else—to adopt a patristic formula—"God became man so that man might become God". In this case the multiplicity of religions presents no problem. A multiplicity of keys was offered to us to open a very complicated lock. Each would turn, more or less, in the key-hole, but in the end none would work. Now we are offered a different kind of key, that of the Man-God. It throws open to us the mystery of Jesus of Nazareth; it throws open the mystery of the eighteen previous centuries of Israel's history; it throws open the mystery of the world and of each of our lives. What need have we now of the other keys which open nothing? What more should we seek if Jesus, and he alone, is God-with-us?

*   *   *

But I think one can convince even those who still shrink from admitting Christ's divinity about Christianity's transcendence. An objective examination of the various religious movements which at present divide the world between them is enough to demonstrate this transcendence. To begin with, the examination is much less difficult than might be supposed. For, apart from minor differences, existing religions (I am even tempted to say "possible" religions) may be legitimately grouped in three categories:

1. Eastern religions, religions of divine immanence.
2. Faith in man and in humanity.
3. Christianity, the free gift of a personal and transcendent God.

I shall not stop to discuss Islam, whatever the (growing) number of its adherents and their possible sanctity. For Islam really derives all its basic elements from Judaism or from Christianity, and offers no fresh solution to the religious problem. Let us, then, consider the three categories one by one.

1. *Eastern religions* (considered, of course, in their specific nature apart from western influences which are beginning to affect them). These religions attract by their insistence on mysticism. Our world, which is glutted with technique, over-occupied with producing utility-articles, living in a whirl of nervous energy, hankers after sources of spiritual refreshment. It relieves its thirst by reading the Hindu mystics, or at least Rabindranath Tagore.[1] Religious souls are naturally susceptible to this discipline of poverty and detachment, which is so close to the Sermon on the Mount and to St Francis of Assisi. They are won over by this faith in the omnipotence of non-resistance.

[1] *Gitanjali* ("Song Offerings") (London, 1914), and *The Fruit Gathering* (London, 1916).

In contrast with the techniques which strive to master nature, the East asks us to renounce all grasping and all possessing so that we may join the ground of all being and so gain the lost Paradise. What better antidote for our materialism could be suggested? What more tremendous possibility of universal and cosmic communion could be offered to a weary and disillusioned race?

But we must show the deceptiveness of this picture and reject it as a mirage. Certainly a discipline of mortification is necessary if man is to free himself from his tendencies to sin, but that is not because matter is a dead weight or an illusion. Certainly man must deny himself so as to go to God, but that is not because activity is—in itself—a bad thing. To consider all human activity as an illusion from which one must free oneself, to believe that our individualities must dissolve into the universal Ego, is to fly in the face of all the laws of life on this planet, to contradict what man is coming more and more to realize as his function and purpose in life. Science as well as Christianity teaches us, more and more clearly every day, that the world has a history, a cosmic, a biological and a human history, and that the fundamental law of this history is a growing complexity which makes possible the growth of consciousness and personality. More and more man recognizes himself as the result of this evolution, or rather as this evolution becomes conscious of itself. Jesus Christ has come to give this evolution a fresh impetus by granting it an infinite term, a share in the very life of the Trinity itself. "See what great love the Father has shown us, that we should be called and should be the children of God" (1 John 3. 1).

Eastern spirituality would lead us by a radically different way, denying the value of personality, of activity and of matter. For the Christian certainly, but also for any man who is aware of biological and human evolution, such a way is nonsensical.

2. *Faith in man and in humanity.* After my examination of contemporary atheism,[1] nobody will consider it surprising that

[1] Cf. Chapter VII.

I should use here the word "faith" and that I should group as "religions" all those movements which make of man or of humanity the only Absolute. *"Homo homini Deus.* The great turning-point of history will be the moment when men will become aware that man's only God is man himself." We are at this turning-point.

African nationalisms or popular democracies, technocracy or Marxism, are among the many different forms in which the same faith in progress, one could almost say the same religion of evolution, is affirmed from one end of the world to the other. (Unless it is not rather the case that this faith is now turning into a disillusioned despair, although men still believe that there is no salvation outside man himself.)

Faith in man, which is no longer confined to the West where it was born, goes in the opposite direction to that current of thought which I have called "Eastern" after its land of origin. The East counselled passivity; the West (and the new East in imitation of it) preaches activity and launches five-year plans. The East despises matter; the West thought only of mastering it and utilizing it. The East was not interested in history; the West considers nothing except the movement of history.

Since we feel ourselves called to a way of life opposed to the Eastern one, are we therefore to take that path on which the West, and the whole world after it, is hurling itself forward? Yes and no. Yes, for we believe—far more than any Marxist—in the movement of history. But a history which leads to no immortality and to no transcendence seems to us very short, very stifling and very disappointing. Our reproach against Marxism is that it robs man of his future. Where does its movement of history lead if humanity—as is certain—will one day disappear altogether? What can the Marxists reply to men like Jean Rostand? And we also reproach the Marxists with crushing the human Person. As Jaspers has said, only Transcendence can save Existence. A system which denies all transcendence ends in the abolition of persons.

Once more the truth of Pascal's remark is shown: "All doctrine is true in what it affirms; false in what it denies."

We need not hesitate to retain the affirmations of Eastern religions: the sense of the All, the necessity for stripping oneself, for poverty and asceticism. We need not hesitate to approve the positive intuitions of the new humanism: its faith in man's possibilities, in the cosmic significance of evolution, in the movement of history. But we are stifled by the negations of these religions or ideologies. And then, even without faith in Christ's divinity, the transcendence of Christianity stares us in the face.

I shall try to make this clear by using an old Eastern fable.

Some blind men are touching an elephant, an animal about which they at present know nothing. One of them gets hold of the trunk and declares that the elephant is a kind of snake. Another finds a leg and is ready to go to the stake for its being a kind of tree. It is a sort of rope for the one who seizes on the tail and a spear for the one who has felt the tusks. For the man who is leaning against it, the elephant is a sort of wall. Only someone who sees can hope to bring the blind men to agree upon the facts. His superiority consists in the fact that his sight enables him to grasp all at once what the others can perceive only partially and—strictly speaking—successively. But above all he resolves the scattered elements into a higher synthesis, that of sight itself.

Christianity has not merely the power to reconcile the West's "faith in the World" and the "ascetic detachment" of the East, or rather it is because it is transcendent that it has this power, and that is something which is less to be "demonstrated" than to be "monstrated". So we must repeat what it is that we believe, if this transcendence is to be apparent.

Saint Paul in the course of a letter to the faithful of Corinth has summed up our faith in three short propositions:

Omnia vestra sunt,

vos autem Christi,

Christus autem Dei.

(1 Cor. 3. 23)

Omnia vestra sunt. The entire universe has been made for man, so as to issue in man, made in the image and likeness of God and appointed to rule over all creatures.[1] Only man explains the universe and gives it meaning and purpose. Man is not an accident in the universe; he is the end of the universe.

Vos autem Christi. Man and the world are not, however, the final goal. Creation is undertaken by God in order to unite with himself in his well-beloved Son beings worthy of his love. If we had a total view of the universe, past, present and future, we should see all the lines of force converging to a meeting-point which gives the world all its consistency, its unity and its value: Jesus Christ. At the centre of the world, as at the heart of our faith, there is the mystery of the Incarnation, the mystery of the Son of God who has come to assume human nature so that man may be "affiliated" in him (*ad Filium*: to give divine Sonship). When Jesus gives his body to his disciples to eat ("This is my body: take, all of you, and eat"), Christ, as St Paul explains,[2] wants us to become his body. *Manducant et manducantur*, said St Thomas Aquinas, following St Augustine. Humanity is gradually "Christified" by the Eucharist. And since all men are bound up with one another and linked physically with the whole cosmos, the entire universe, through man and through the Man-God, is turned towards the Father. *Christus autem Dei.*

We can no longer abstain from a passionate interest in the growth of man and the development of the universe, since the world groans in travail, waiting for the glorious liberty of the sons of God.

Nevertheless an ascesis is indispensable, both for freeing ourselves from sin, which is slavery and a corruption of God's kingdom, and for accepting the "Paschal mystery" of a world which must be associated with the death and resurrection of Christ if it is to break forth at last into glory.

* * *

What, then, of the multiplicity of religions? Why do we still need these little points of light when we have God's sunshine?

[1] Gen. 1. 26–7.
[2] 1 Cor. 10. 16–17.

CHAPTER XII

SALVATION OUTSIDE THE CHURCH

The considerations of the previous chapter, in so far as they show the transcendence of Christianity, make all the more urgent a problem which would require a whole volume if we treated it exhaustively but which we cannot pass by: the problem of salvation outside the visible Church.

The well-known axiom "Outside the Church no salvation" seems to be a faithful translation of the words of Jesus himself: "He who believes and is baptized will be saved, he who refuses belief will be condemned" (Mark 16. 16). In a book called *What is Faith?* we cannot avoid the question: "What is the faith which is necessary for salvation?" On the one hand, we declare that God is love and that he wills to save all men by Jesus Christ.[1] On the other hand, it is quite clear not only that most of mankind have not been baptized, but that very many—the majority? —are unable to know Jesus Christ. It seems obvious that nobody can be condemned unless he has sinned against the light. And the Church herself has declared heretical Saint-Cyran's statement "not one drop of grace falls upon pagans".

An incident in the life of St Pius X will show us in what spirit we should approach the problem of the salvation of "infidels":

[1] God, our Saviour, wills that all should be saved and come to the knowledge of the truth. For there is only one God; and only one mediator between God and men, the man Christ Jesus (1 Tim. 2. 4).

I remember [Mgr Rosa deposed at the process of canoniza-
tion] that I was walking with him in Mantua when he was still
a Cardinal. We found ourselves in front of the Jews' cemetery.
The servant of God suddenly asked me in a serious tone of voice
whether I had said a *De profundis* for those who were buried
there. I said that I had not, because they had either died with
the desire for baptism, in which case they were already in
heaven, or else they had not this desire, in which case prayer
for them was useless. Without making an immediate reply, he
raised his hat and at once started the *De profundis*, in which I
naturally joined. At the end of it he put on his hat and said with
a smile: "Well, we have done our part; the Lord will do his. For
it is nowhere said that the Lord's theology is like that of the
Jesuits at the Gregorian University" (I had only just finished
my studies there).

(*Processus ordinarius romanus*, II, p. 1039.)

I shall consider two questions in order:
1. What relationship to the Church is necessary for salvation?
2. What sort of faith does this relationship imply?

*   *   *

I. *What relationship to the Church is necessary for salvation?* I must reply for a start that we cannot be saved outside
the Church if we give this name to the "Body of Christ". God's
plan is to make us his sons by incorporating us with his well-
beloved Son (Eph. 1. 3–12), to "affiliate" us in his Son. If the
Church is "Jesus Christ spread abroad and communicated",
if it is the "whole Christ", or again "the body of Christ", it is
clear that to be incorporated into Christ and to be incorporated
into the Church is the same thing.

But many do not visibly belong to the Catholic and Roman
Church. Are we going to say that they cannot belong to the
body of Christ, or shall we say with Simone Weil that all
religious confessions, indeed all religious philosophies, form a
single church in which we may find God?

A formula which claims to resolve the difficulty is still some-times in evidence. A distinction is made between the "body of the Church", the Roman Church, and the "soul of the Church", the "mystical body". You have only to look carefully at these words to see the implicit contradiction. It is impossible to dis-tinguish the body of the Church from the body of Christ, and Pius XII in his Encyclical *Mystici Corporis Christi* makes it quite clear that there is identity between the mystical body of Christ and the Catholic and Roman Church.

The true solution seems to be that Christians separated from Rome and pagans can belong *invisibly* to the *visible* Church. (Obviously the relationship is a more intimate one in the case of Christians than it is for Mohammedans, Buddhists, etc.) An illustration may make this easier to understand. In the days before radio was used for navigation, a ship was battling against a storm. On board, as well as the crew, there were passengers, more or less inexperienced. The goodwill of these was often shown in unhelpful ways. The ship's safety depended on the discipline and devotion of the crew. But all who remained on the ship were saved along with it. Only those were irremediably lost who refused all "transcendent" salvation and threw them-selves into the water, not wishing to rely on anything save their own powers. For humanity, to apply this illustration to the matter in hand, there is no salvation outside the vessel which is saved by the visible Roman Church. But the visible Church saves every soul of good will. That is to say that all grace of salvation comes from the Church and tends to the Church. All grace comes from the Church: the Church is the mediatrix of grace because she is the body of Christ, the sole mediator. And all grace tends to the Church in the sense that both for the honour of the passengers and for the success of the crew's manoeuvres everyone must collaborate to the best of his ability in saving the vessel.

Another comparison has been suggested to show that all grace tends to the Church. During an evacuation in wartime, a father and mother lost one of their children. Long afterwards they discovered that a family had taken it in and looked after it very well. Did they not, all the same, want to have it back in the bosom of their own family?

Is it necessary to add that, conversely, it is not sufficient for salvation to belong visibly to the Church? These words of St Augustine are clear enough: "How many are there who are not ours and yet seem to be in the bosom of the Church, and how many are there who are ours and seem to be outside the Church! ... How many wolves in the sheepfold, how many sheep outside it!" I am reminded of the words written by Rouault on one of his engravings of the *Miserere*: "The gentlewoman has a reserved seat in heaven"!

But the second question remains unanswered.

*   *   *

2. *What sort of faith does this relationship imply?*

There can be no question of an explicit faith in Christ and in the Trinity. The Epistle to the Hebrews (11. 6) gives an answer to our question: "Without faith it is impossible to please him. To go to God it is necessary to believe that he exists and that he is a rewarder of those who seek him." It is necessary to "believe that God exists" and "to seek him as the Supreme Good". These propositions are wonderfully enlightening and liberating. We find again here the distinction which was made between the "closed" soul and the "open" one.

The "closed" soul, the soul turned in on itself, the intelligence closed in upon itself which disregards all the great avenues leading outwards to the infinite, the closed heart which refers the name of love only to selfish and sensual possessing, how can these receive the gift of God? The sin against the Holy Spirit which immures the soul in itself, the sin which is the source of all sins, is a life without adventure and without love, a life of self-satisfaction.

Faith is laying oneself open to dissatisfaction and to desire.

Faith is readiness to set out on the journey, to go further and further.

Faith is the search for God in the knowledge that he exists and that he alone can demand everything and promise everything, take everything and give everything.

CHAPTER XIII

THE LIFE OF FAITH

When we hear people say: "I have lost my faith" or "I have found faith again" one gets the impression that faith, for them, is a sort of object which can be lost and found again, like a key or a pencil. So far I have myself talked too much of faith as if it were a monolithic block, which is either just there or just not there; whereas one ought to think of faith as a living reality, always fragile, always threatened, constantly growing and constantly changing. When Jesus asked his apostles whether they had faith, St Peter replied with much modesty and appropriateness: "Lord, increase our faith."

Faith is an encounter with the living God; it means letting God in. An encounter between two persons is always something mysterious and ineffable. And if one of the two persons is God . . . ? We know to our cost that there is never anything fixed and final between two persons. We know also that intimacy can grow indefinitely. So there is a *life* of faith. I do not mean merely a life which is illumined by faith or a life which springs from faith (*Justus ex fide vivit*), but the life of faith itself, with its birth, its sickness, its growing pains, its frustrations and its smooth waters. There are no general laws about this. The encounter between God and each person is a mystery which cannot be put into any category. The analyses on which we shall embark must respect this truth; they are meant only to promote the reflections of the reader himself upon his own "sacred history".

I. *Conversion*

All conversions are different. Each is a unique case, for each soul, like each destiny, is unique. Only God is the same in every conversion, and the nature of the faith which the convert attains. That is why there are nevertheless "constants" in all conversions.

First of all there cannot be a desire for faith without an encounter which shows the soul the existence of a fresh dimension in the world. Take someone who was living a human existence moulded by his education, formed by his environment, animated by a few personal convictions, without anything in his behaviour to suggest a more than human vision. He meets a genuine Christian who reveals to him another dimension of existence and so raises a doubt about the principles on which his life was based. It may be an indifference to money or other material goods or an extraordinary independence of judgement, a habitual self-mastery or a readiness to listen to people and to help them when there is need; perhaps it is simply a straightforward look or a certain calm joyfulness . . . anyhow there is something mysterious about this soul, something which is beyond one, like a well which is too deep to measure. Furthermore, such a man seems to be "indwelt" by the mysterious presence of an Other to whom he occasionally refers in an off-hand way. A question becomes inevitable: whence does he derive this joy, this peace, this power and this light? If such an encounter takes place with other men who also call themselves Christians, it seems that the question bears on Christianity itself, and the desire to know about this religion comes to birth.

At this point all sorts of obstacles arise: the dumbness of Christians or the hopelessly poor answers they give, the scandal caused by so many Catholics whose conduct contradicts what that of a few saints suggests, the hideousness of so many churches, the reactionary politics of a good many Catholics, the apparent absurdity of the dogmas which they profess. . . . All these reasons, or all these pretexts, combine to deter one from an inquiry which threatens to make alarming changes in a man's life. The soul is torn between contradictory desires, and, alas, only too often there is nobody to help: it is so difficult, when one is an unbeliever, to talk to a priest; and lay people seem so unwilling to talk about God. At most they are prepared to tell you about dogmas, or moral principles, or ceremonies. Even if you can find a Christian who can speak of God and of Jesus Christ, there is a long struggle ahead, Jacob's struggle with the Angel, which may last for years. Rimbaud and Claudel have said: "The spiritual combat is as brutal as human warfare." Desire and disgust, light and darkness, alternate; but during this time of waiting a Presence becomes more and more real, from which you know you cannot escape. Often it proves to be at the time of the last revolt that a man will fall on his knees, saying with Thomas: "My Lord and my God!"

But from this moment intense peace and joy fill the soul, and whatever setbacks and intellectual difficulties occur the essential truth will never be doubted again. This seems to me a point of great importance in regard to the objectivity of faith. If it were a matter of construction on the part of the subject, in the first place it would vary with individuals instead of coinciding with the whole faith professed by the Church; further, it would not stand the test of time. But among dozens of adult converts with whom I have kept closely in touch, none has cast doubt on the encounter which he had made with the living God.

It is rash in the extreme to put the conditions for conversion into a formula. Yet experience does suggest that three conditions are necessary and sufficient, if a soul is to encounter God; each is necessary and together they are sufficient. They are prayer, the love and the genuine knowledge of Jesus Christ. I have explained at length why prayer is the absolute condition of all conversion: prayer is the very expression of a need for transcendence and for opening the soul to God. God can enter a soul only if it is not closed by self-satisfaction, but freely open to his love. Secondly, it is quite clear that only love opens to substantial Love. And lastly, we cannot go to the

Father except by meeting and getting to know Jesus Christ. These considerations show us the sort of collaboration which God expects from us if we are to help our brethren. With entire respect for their liberty and with profound understanding of their difficulties, bearing in mind the inevitable delays of spiritual growth and without trying to forestall Providence, we should reveal to our unbelieving brethren the true face of Jesus Christ. If our faith is a living experience for us, we shall not be able to speak of Jesus Christ without living ourselves by prayer and love. It will then be natural for us to ask our brethren to join us in this prayer and love.

II. *The age for conversion to Jesus Christ is between eighteen and twenty-five*

I am no longer speaking of unbelievers, but of the baptized, of practising Catholics. Between the age of eighteen and that of twenty-five certain changes must come about, apart from which religion will remain an affair of the nursery and of environment, destined to disappear or to become sterile conformism. Here again it is difficult, and quite inadequate, to put this conversion into a formula. I shall not try to do more than give two snapshots, from two different positions, of a reality which is far more complex than my illustrations of it.

1. The Christian "way of life" should be discovered between the age of eighteen and that of twenty-five (but, of course, better later than never!). This formula is less paradoxical than it at first appears. If God makes us live a certain number of years on this earth, it is probably because these years are necessary (normally) for the full development of our faith. Our life is not a sort of carpet with a surface which is uniformly suitable for the developing of our spiritual muscles. (After that the carpet could be rolled up and thrown away!) Our whole lives are the work of God, and every period of life brings its materials for a construction which is to be preserved in its entirety. I shall speak later of the final stages of life and the graces which

they bring with them. For the moment I shall confine myself to childhood, adolescence and youth.

It seems that we can speak of three sorts of morality which normally belong to these three stages of life. The child can hardly be aware of anything save what he is told to do or forbidden to do, and, for a time, the distinction between right and wrong is something which he finds out from his teachers, his conscience being for the present only the reflection of their teaching. So the child lives in subjection to a sort of highway code; you must keep to the left, stop at the red light, etc.... It is obvious that some adults have never got beyond that; they are adults physically, but children in moral matters. In the confessional they will not fail to accuse themselves of eating meat on Friday or missing Mass on Sunday. But it never occurs to them to accuse themselves of taking no part in the struggle for a better world or of keeping their superfluities for themselves.

The adolescent is capable of a much higher morality than the child. He becomes enthusiastic for an ideal. He admires heroes whom he wants to imitate. He feels himself capable of heroic actions. He has reached the age of morality proper to the hero and the sage. He feels his failures bitterly sometimes, and feels himself hopelessly torn between his ideal and his instincts. If he is a "nice chap", he will never dare to say, with his hand on his heart, like some self-satisfied adults, that he has nothing to reproach himself with. He feels the discrepancy between his ideal and his wretchedness too keenly. If only all adults could keep (or discover) this flame of heroism and sincerity which burns in so many of the young! And yet—however surprising it may seem—this morality of the hero and the sage is a long way from Christian morality.

A morality is "Christian" only in so far as it comes from Christ, the Son of God made man. Jesus is not a sort of "Christian Socrates" proposing to us a moral ideal; he does not only teach us to love one another. If Jesus had come only to offer us a human ideal, God could have done without the

Incarnation; some prophet would have sufficed, or even a sage. Jesus did not come to teach us a way. He *is* the Way. He did not come to propose an ideal of life to us. He *is* Life. That is to say that there is no "Christian" morality save that which consists in the animating of our lives by Christ. In my life, all is sin which is put in brackets, withdrawn from Christ's animation—not only everything which is contrary to Christ's will for me, but also everything which is dead wood, everything which the sap of Christ does not animate. "Sin" is of an order quite different from that of a "fault" against an ideal, still more different from that of an "infringement" against a highway code. We do not receive the sacrament of penance in order to get back our moral good looks. We come to meet the God of love so that he may restore us to his love, by reviving the energy through which we were converted to him.

The criterion of an adult faith—or at least one of them—is the realization of sin in the sense just described, for this implies that we have discovered Christ as the controller of our lives and that in spite of all our shortcomings and weaknesses we have allowed him to animate our existences. Apart from that how could one speak of a genuine faith?

2. To be an adult is to be responsible. Nobody would dream of contesting this formula in regard to our everyday affairs; you become an adult when you have responsibility in your job, your home, your country.... How is it that so few Christians think of applying this definition to the sphere of their faith? Almighty God has done us the grace and the honour of making us free, of putting into our own hands not only our individual destinies, but even the destiny of his Kingdom. He has made us "cooperators" (1 Cor. 3. 9). How can we pretend to have an adult faith if we are not aware of our responsibilities?

My responsibility for myself comes first, that is, in the sphere of faith, my responsibility for the life of God in me. Faith will be living in me only if I make it live, that is to say—in the language of the previous paragraph—if I subject my life to Christ's animation. Here we can be altogether concrete and, at the same time, exhaustive. There are four absolutely inseparable conditions to be fulfilled if my life is to be animated by Christ, if I am to become a sharer in Christ's mystery:

Hearing the Word of God.

Prayer.

The sacraments.

Love of my neighbour.

These have only to be enumerated for it to be quite clear that they are all necessary to this bond between Christ and ourselves. There is no need to emphasize, for example, that the sacraments are the expression and the realization of this communion with Christ. We may dare to compare it with the conjugal act as the expression and normal realization of the communion between husband and wife. But it does seem necessary to insist that the four conditions cannot be dissociated from one another. They are not like four drawers any one of which you can pull out at will. They are like the dimensions of one and the same volume, which you can certainly take up on this side or on that but which you must move in its entirety if you move it at all. There is no true prayer without hearing the word of God. There is no efficacious sacrament without prayer. And there is no true religious life which is not expressed in love of one's neighbour.

Thus there is no divine life in me unless I feel myself, in the world in which I live, the most responsible of men. It is difficult, when you think of it, to imagine the thoughtlessness which can allow us to say "Father, may your Kingdom come", while not lifting a finger to help its coming. The absenteeism of Christians, not only in regard to apostolic duties, but even in regard to civic and social ones, their indifference to injustice and oppression, seem to unbelievers, quite reasonably, a proof of the inconsistency of this faith which—in theory—they profess.

The faith of an adult will be unreal if it is not inspiring his temporal activity. A man between twenty-five and forty-five is a constructor in a field of family, civic and professional activities. What sort of a faith would he have if it did not animate

these human responsibilities? It would be no faith at all or—
which is worse—it would be a lie. A Christian whose professional and civic life is not animated by his faith is in grave
sin, however devout he may seem on Sundays. And if ever this
Christian "engagement", or (in Emmanuel Mounier's phrase)
"Christian confrontation", was necessary, it is certainly today.
From the neolithic age onwards men lived a life in cities and
villages which was more or less fixed to the soil and isolated.
For several centuries, and above all in our own, a sort of thaw
has been taking place which is becoming an avalanche. Men
are becoming aware of their unity for the first time in their
history. Who is going to have an outlook wide enough and
generous enough to help the world in its labour, who, if not
Christians? If Christians do not come to the rescue, if they let
this hour, which is their own, go by, the Church will be practically swept away from a world which will be made without it.
And the unreal faith of the sham Christians will vanish like
smoke in the wind.

The faith of an adult can only be a faith which is "engaged".
The sanctity of a layman in the twentieth century can only
be that of a man who is "engaged" by his faith in a Christian
"confrontation".

III. *The crises of faith and the ages of faith*

Faith, like love, is something alive, which is fragile and constantly threatened. Like everything alive, faith is threatened
from within and from without. What has been said about the
close connection between hearing the word of God, prayer, the
sacraments and love of one's neighbour makes it unnecessary
to explain all the crises of faith which arise from the absence
of one or more of these sources of life. A fire cannot be expected to burn without fuel. It is not surprising that love should
be quenched when one party cuts off all relations with the other.
Why are Christians surprised to find their faith extinguished if
there is nothing to feed it? Why should all jobs mean work
except the "job" of being a Christian?

But, in addition to these crises which are only too easy to explain, there are all those which come from outside, that is, from events or from doctrines which are in violent contradiction with our faith.

Many crises of faith arise from great suffering or from the scandal of evil in the world. I have considered this problem from an intellectual point of view. It is only in the light of faith itself and in prayer that this sort of crisis can be overcome and can lead to a truer faith in the mystery of Christ's death and resurrection.

Other crises arise from the opposition between our faith and world-views which seem—or actually are—in contradiction with it: Marxism, for example, and certain pseudo-scientific syntheses. There is no need to repeat what was said about present-day atheism. I shall just make the point that none of these crises should be without fruit. Every error is the misuse of a truth. The element of truth which every system contains is often an occasion of purifying our faith from accretions or seeing it against a background wider than we had once thought necessary. Let me take two quite simple examples. For a century now many Christians have been troubled in their faith by doctrines of evolution. They had attached their belief to conservative views on this subject according to which every animal species, and man's body in particular, sprang from the Creator's hand in its definitive form. They thought it against Catholic teaching that various forms of life should be engendered from one another and, in the end, produce man. And unbelievers were not slow to rub this in. It took a long time for these Christians to accept two pieces of evidence. The first, belonging to the scientific order, is that there is a "history of life", that all beings belong to a spatio-temporal continuity. The second, of the theological order, is that God is no less the first cause because there are secondary ones; in other words, that God is no less the Creator if he makes beings make themselves than if he made them directly, short-circuiting secondary causes. So our faith required a double purification. It had to be dissociated from a whole pseudo-scientific outlook which had really nothing to do with it, and which, furthermore, was false. Our faith in God the Creator appears to us today far more luminous now that it is projected on the splendid screen of an evolutionary world (always provided that we avoid the fresh confusion of identifying the data of our faith with new scientific discoveries).

A similar difficulty arose out of biblical criticism and still disturbs some believers who were brought up to think of God's Word as proceeding without intermediary from the mouth of the Almighty. When criticism showed the relatively late composition of certain texts, the use of profane sources, borrowings from other cultures, the projection upon the events of an epoch of much later ideas and institutions, etc. . . . these people were troubled in their faith. They had forgotten that God acts through secondary causes, and that the Bible is an entirely human book as well as an entirely divine one. Eventually the work of criticism sifts the faith itself from all foreign elements, and above all it enables us to appreciate the admirable divine pedagogy which can use all human initiatives and enlist them in the service of the Lord's Epiphany. The task is far from being completed, especially as regards the New Testament. We can await further results not only calmly but exultantly, knowing that in the end our faith can only be the gainer, whatever difficulties we may have for the moment in adapting our minds to new views.

The crises which these two examples have illustrated spring from causes which are exterior to the believer and, in a sense, independent of him. But the faithful themselves pass through varying stages of life, and their faith must be constantly renewed, adapted to the new man who is called into being by every one of these stages. There cannot be a faith which is acquired unchangeably once and for all, any more than there can be a love which is fixed once and for all between two lovers. Husband and wife do not love as they did when they were first engaged; their love is different when they are expecting their first child, and will be quite different again when they have several children. It is not the same in youth as in old age, etc. . . . So the faith of a mature man, or of the aged, is different from that of a young man.

I have spoken of the faith of the young man who has passed through the sociological habits of infancy and the subjective idealism of adolescence to find the reality of the living God. He gives himself with enthusiasm and generosity to the Jesus who speaks to him the words of eternal Life and promises him—in return for a total renunciation—a hundredfold in this world. Happy are they who have had such an experience, which will leave a mark upon all their later life. And yet this enthusiasm will not last indefinitely. The honeymoon was necessary; but it is no more the fullness of love than the happiness of the young married couple. Just as the difficulties of married life purify and deepen love, so the disillusionment which life brings with it purifies and deepens faith. In a young man's enthusiasm there is still a good deal of idealism, and what he calls faith in God is often only confidence in his own superabundant vital powers. The young, overflowing with energy and hungry for the infinite, are easily generous and readily exclaim, *Laetus obtuli universa!* It will be more difficult for them to give, day after day, what they have offered all at once . . . and in words. And then there are the failures and disappointments which multiply, those which come from outside and those which result from our inward wretchedness. Nearly all converts have to go through a crisis after about a year of fervour; prayer becomes difficult, attempts to lead a stricter and more generous life become less and less successful; the great discoveries with which faith dazzled their eyes are all over; they slip into lukewarmness. Faith and certitude remain intact, but illusions vanish. The spade comes up against rock. There is great danger of giving up the struggle and settling down to a sceptical and disillusioned sort of existence. The problem is not that of maintaining a juvenile fault, but of passing beyond it, recognizing the "impurity" in an enthusiasm which was animated rather by one's own vitality than by the breath of the Holy Spirit. If, as I have said, to have faith is to put one's centre of gravity in God and not in oneself, a young man is not habitually capable of it. A grim struggle with reality is needed to dis-appropriate us little by little of ourselves. The sun must first sink if the stars are to shine in the night. We have to lose a certain confidence in ourselves if we are to rely on God.

Let us follow this thought to the end. I have quoted from Exodus: "No one can see God without dying" (33. 20). When a man has passed fifty, objective reality begins to lose its con-sistency, and eternity becomes more present to him. Its light bathes the passing moment more and more. Faith becomes more serene and more luminous.

None of these stages, of course, is an automatic affair. Every-thing is grace and cooperates with our spiritual development only on the condition that we throw ourselves open, by prayer, to God's action. But if everything is prayer then everything is grace.

CHAPTER XIV

FAITH IS A GIFT OF GOD

Christians may be astonished and scandalized to find this heading to the last chapter but one of this book. Should it not have been stated on the first page that faith is a gift of God? From the theological point of view this complaint is perfectly legitimate. But, when we are addressing unbelievers in the first place, we run the risk of being misunderstood if we tell them at the outset that faith is a gift of God. What meaning can these words have for them? The result might be to bring the conversation to an end and to discourage further enquiry. All the same I did not conceal the truth which the heading of this chapter now states categorically; I put it into equivalent terms by talking about an encounter in which God takes and keeps the initiative, and I did not hesitate to quote the very definite statements of Councils: not only the development but the very beginning of faith and even the inclination to believe are gifts of grace (cf. Chapter V). But I must now bring out the meaning of these truths.

Faith is doubly a gift of God. In the first place God has taken the free initiative of revealing himself to us as a matter of history; this revelation is the gift of God. Then it is the Holy Spirit who enables us to receive this gift of revelation and to have faith. A sort of interior revelation must be added to the revelation which strikes our ears, if we are to believe. Let us consider these two gifts separately.

1. *God has revealed himself to us in a free gift.*[1]

[1] On all this read the excellent paper No. 3 in the first series of *Eléments de doctrine spirituelle*, "Révélation, amour, mystère."

All persons are mysterious and unknowable. "You will not know my secret unless I consent to reveal it to you. If you are to read my soul I must lift the veil. I shall do so if I wish, and I should not do so unless I loved you." If everyone's secret belongs to himself, this must be still more the case with God. Revelation is the unveiling of God's mystery.

God has revealed himself, has spoken to us, by the events of sacred history and by the prophets who have given us the meaning of this history. He has spoken to us by his Word made flesh, Jesus Christ. And the Church transmits to us God's living Word through two agencies sent by Jesus Christ to continue and to complete his work: the apostles and the Holy Spirit. We must realize that Jesus Christ, having given to the Church its definitive structure (constituted by the apostolic college, revelation and the sacraments) went up to heaven to send us the Holy Spirit so that he might bring this revelation into the hearts of all the faithful and so make salvation theirs. Thus, while the apostles and their successors prolong the preaching of Christ throughout human history, the Holy Spirit aids them in their ministry and makes their hearers ready to receive the divine message. So, at the heart of the Church's mystery, there is the combined action of these two "vicars" of Christ, the apostolic college and the Holy Spirit, the latter working within what the former works without, the latter doing divinely what the former does humanly.

But the apostles are what they are through the Holy Spirit. Jesus has linked the witness of the apostles with that of the Holy Spirit: "When the Spirit of truth comes, who proceeds from the Father, he shall bear testimony of me, and you too shall bear testimony of me" (John 15. 26-7). In fact the Holy Spirit and the Apostolate were manifested together at Pentecost. It is the Spirit, fully given to the world only at Pentecost, who makes the apostles speak and bear effective witness. And the Spirit's activity enables the apostles to be more than witnesses of the events and words which they report. Their announcement of the messianic events brings about the accomplishment of these events.

That is certainly the conviction of John and of Peter:

"What we have heard, what we have seen with our eyes, what we beheld and our hands handled of the Word of life ... we announce to you, that you may be in communion with us, and we [by the Spirit] are in communion with the Father and with his Son Jesus Christ" (1 John 1. 1–3).

"The God of our fathers has raised up Jesus Christ. . . . Of these things we are witnesses together with the Holy Spirit whom God has given to those who obey him" (Acts 5. 30–2).

So the work of salvation begins with the Father ("the Father has so loved the world that he has given his Son"), is realized by the Son, and is "completed" by the Spirit sent by the Father and the Son. Revelation, although it is accomplished in Jesus Christ, is not a gift of God given once for all. It is the continual gift of the Spirit.

It is in the liturgy above all that the Word of God is transmitted for us to hear. It is of the greatest importance that the Word of God should be proclaimed and that we should receive it with our ears. The eye is a critic and a possessor; the ear is receptive and believing. There is all the difference between reading a piece of news in the paper and hearing it announced by a witness. The Church is God's witness, announcing to us the good news of the Kingdom and making it as it were sacramentally present to us *hodie*:

> Hodie *Christus natus est nobis*
> *Pridie quam pateretur, hoc est* hodie ...
> Hodie *Christus resurgit.*

The decree of 1956 about the new rites of Holy Week goes so far as to speak of the "sacramental" efficacy of liturgical offices, which amounts to saying that the Holy Spirit is at work in the proclamation of the events of salvation, as he is at work in the sacraments. We see to what extent revelation is a continual gift of God, through the Holy Spirit who is always at work in its proclamation.

*   *   *

2. But it must be added that faith is not only a gift of God in the mouth of the preacher. It is also a gift of God in the ear of the hearer. There is an activity of the Holy Spirit within the souls of those who hear the word of God, and this activity is even more indispensable to faith than the activity of the Holy Spirit exercised upon the apostles. An invisible preacher gives the hearer the grace to adhering to the revelation preached by the apostle. The Holy Spirit performs within souls a work corresponding to that which the apostolate performs externally. Further, even in regard to the apostolic college, the Holy Spirit preserves a sort of freedom and autonomy. There are cases in which an apostle is not necessary for faith, whereas faith is always the work of the Holy Spirit; it can happen that the Spirit does not work in and through the institution of the Church, but otherwise. Thus Paul was converted on the road to Damascus without any intervention on the part of the apostolic college. Faith is always a gift of the Holy Spirit who reserves the right to immediate and personal action.

Let us consider more closely this necessary activity of the Spirit:

No one knows the things of God, except the Spirit of God (1 Cor. 2. 11).

No one can come to me, unless the Father who has sent me draw him (John 6. 44).

These two sentences, one Paul's, the other spoken by Jesus himself, leave no room for doubt. Even more striking perhaps is the declaration made by Jesus to Peter when he had confessed that he was the Messias, the Son of the living God:

"Blessed are you, Simon, son of Jonas, for this revelation is not of flesh and blood, but of my Father who is in heaven." Simon, son of Jonas, is only a weak man, enclosed within the limits of the human. Only God could give him access to a truth which only he knows. Neither miracles nor the most formal declarations by Jesus himself could give Peter faith. All that provided him with reasons for believing, but these reasons are not faith and cannot attain to faith. Peter's faith in Christ's divinity is not a human conviction. It comes from God. It is a gift of God.

The words used by Jesus imply, too, much more than an intellectual illumination: "No one can come to me, unless the Father draw him". At this point we really need St Augustine's commentary on these words in its entirety. But here are a few lines of it:

> Do not suppose that you have been drawn against your will, for the soul lets itself be drawn by love. In saying this we should not have the slightest fear of those who weigh each word, but are a hundred leagues away from religious truth, and object: "How, if I am thus drawn, can I believe by my own will?"
>
> I tell you: not only are you drawn by the will but also by delight... there is a delight of the heart.... If poets have said that each of us is drawn by delight, by pleasure, much more ought we to say that a man is drawn to Jesus Christ when he is delighted by the truth, delighted by eternal life.... Give me a lover and he will understand what I say; give me someone who has a desire, a hunger and thirst for the heavenly country, and he will know what I mean....
>
> Show a sheep a green bough, and it will follow you; show a child nuts and it will follow you. It is drawn by love; it is drawn without any physical violence.... Will not Jesus Christ, revealed by the Father, have this power to draw?[1]

And again:

> If you are not drawn, pray that you may be.

That is the very practical conclusion. To the extent that we understand that faith is a gift of God, we understand that, for others and for ourselves, prayer is the only way which leads to it, and the only way in which it can grow.

* * *

For the Holy Spirit's activity is not confined to conversion. It animates all our life of faith. The Spirit makes us grow more and more out of a purely conceptual adherence into an "intelli-

[1] *Tract. in Jo.* 25. 4–5.

gence" of the revealed mysteries. It leads us into "the whole truth", as Jesus promised and as it came about in tremendous fashion at Pentecost. The Spirit makes this or that phrase in the Bible, which had before only a purely intellectual content for one, suddenly come alive and fill one with emotion. It is no longer merely the objective statement of a truth which is properly understood; it is now a word which God speaks to me in the centre of my soul and which issues in joy and certitude. We can hardly fail to think of Pascal's memorial, quoted at the beginning of this book. Through the Holy Spirit the knowledge of God tends to become experimental. This does not mean an immediate vision of God or a sensible perception of his presence. It means that a mere knowledge of doctrinal facts changes gradually into a synthetic and harmonious view of the mysteries of God and of his Kingdom. Above all we experience in ourselves a vital dynamism, and we gain a certitude which transcends all human certitudes.

Finally, is it enough to say that faith is a "gift of God"? It is also a sharing in the knowledge with which God knows himself. Hence that security which stupefies—and sometimes exasperates—the unbeliever, who cannot understand, on the human level, the Vatican Council's bold declaration:

"Those who have received faith through the teachings of the Church can never have any just cause for changing their faith or calling it in question" (Constitution de fide, Chap. III).

Notice the way in which the Council connects the faith of each individual and that of the whole Church. Both are the work of one and the same Spirit. What the Holy Spirit accomplishes in each of the faithful he accomplishes in the whole Church, creating in all the unanimity of one same faith. The Spirit makes the Church infallible in its entirety and as such, by the two combined activities mentioned in Chapter X: the Spirit makes the apostolic hierarchy infallible so that it may transmit the deposit of faith to the whole body and declare its genuine meaning; and, secondly, the Spirit makes the whole body of the Church infallible so as to believe and to live this faith, the objective determinations of which are provided by the apostolic hierarchy.

*   *   *

So by saying that faith is a gift of God we express a reality—as much an individual as a collective affair—which is nothing less than a part of the Holy Spirit's mission, fulfilling those of the Father and the Son.

"May the love of the Father, the grace of the Lord Jesus Christ, and the communion (or communication) of the Holy Spirit be with you all", says St Paul at the end of one of his letters (2 Cor. 13. 13).

After putting all this emphasis upon the Holy Spirit's activity it is desirable to add, without taking back anything but in order to avoid any misunderstanding, that the faithful remain none the less entirely free, active and responsible.

1. From the fact that faith is a gift of God it does not follow that we are not responsible for not having it.

For to say that God refuses faith to this person or that would be to admit that he condemns them by denying them the means of justification.

Such a proposition is as contrary to the declaration of the Councils as it is to those of Scripture. God summons all men to salvation, and so to faith. Therefore he gives to each one the possibility of having at least that faith necessary to salvation which was discussed in Chapter XII, where it was said that it is necessary to believe in one "God who gives rewards to those who seek him" (Heb. 11. 6). The sun shines for all, but those who shut themselves up in cellars or draw their blinds receive no benefit from it.

2. From the fact that faith is a gift of God it does not follow that the believer is "passive". The lamp shines thanks to the electric current which is *given* to it. The disciple understands thanks to the teaching which is *given* to him. The lamp and the disciple use, actualize, the gift which they have received. Our

Protestant brethren regularly suppose that the cooperation of man takes away from God's transcendence, as if God's activity and man's were on the same level. Certainly if two horses are pulling a carriage you can work out that the stronger is doing sixty per cent. of the work and the weaker forty per cent. But when I write with my pen, it is one hundred per cent. myself writing, and one hundred per cent. the pen. The lamplight is one hundred per cent. due to the current, and one hundred per cent. to the lamp. All the more, when it is a question of God's activity in us, all is from God and all from us. In philosophical language we may say that transcendence and immanence are perfectly compatible.

We shall be judged by our works, and in the first place by our acceptance or rejection of the faith given by God. But we are not saved by works but by faith which, operating in charity, fructifies in our works. And, clearly, what is true of the original acquisition of faith is true also of its growth in us.

We must always come back to Bergson's words about the soul "which is both acting and acted upon, whose freedom coincides with God's divinity".

CHAPTER XV

THE DEFINITION OF FAITH

The various approaches which we have made to the mystery of faith prepare us for the definition of faith given to us by the Vatican Council (1870), which I now propose to utilize. In the midst of all the negations of the nineteenth century the Church thought it necessary to make its position plain in regard to the current pretensions or abdications of the human reason, and to pinpoint faith. These are the Council's actual words:

> Faith is a supernatural virtue,
> by which, guided and aided by divine grace,
> we hold as true what God has revealed,
> not because we have perceived its intrinsic
> truth by our reason
> but because of the authority of God
> who can neither deceive nor be deceived.[1]

I shall comment on this definition.

A supernatural virtue. The wholly human and at the same time wholly divine character of faith is thus declared. Faith is a virtue; so it requires man's free cooperation and the exercise of his will (*virtus* in Latin implies the idea of energy, of virility —from the root *vir*). The life of faith constantly demands from us energy and courage. But faith is a "supernatural" virtue, which surpasses man's possibilities, and which can only be the fruit of God's gift. The Church also tells us that faith is a "theological" virtue, which has God as its object and as its cause. Faith is, properly speaking, a communication to man of

[1] Session III, cap. 3 (Denzinger, 1789).

God's own knowledge of himself. That is the Father's plan, realized by the Son and communicated by the Holy Spirit.

Guided and aided by grace. As I have said so often, God always keeps the initiative. I now add to the passage of the Council of Orange quoted in Chapter V this further passage from the same Council (can. 6):

> If anyone says that God has mercy on us, when, without God's grace, we believe, will, desire, make efforts, labour, watch, study, ask, seek and knock, and does not confess that we believe, will and do all these things, as we should, through the infusion of the Holy Spirit and his inspiration, or if anyone makes the help of grace depend upon humility or human obedience, instead of admitting that it is a gift of grace itself that we are humble and obedient, he resists the Apostle who says: "What have you that you have not received?" "It is by the grace of God that I am what I am."[1]

We hold as true what God has revealed. Faith is an act of the intelligence, which is the faculty of the truth. Nothing is falser than to relegate faith to the realm of sentiment and to deprive it of its intellectual content. That is why we cannot follow certain of our Protestant brethren who separate "faith" from "belief", continuing the dissociation effected by Luther between a pure act of God and a merely human and carnal reality. Faith, in this account, is the act of God in us which makes us adhere to him. Belief would have to do with a human formulation, something inadequate, contingent and perpetually reformable. Karl Barth has given a fresh emphasis to this idea in the words: "To say that God reveals himself means that he himself intervenes, as both the knower and the known, the speaker and the hearer." Protestantism has never recognized that Jesus, to communicate the faith to the faithful, uses the twin "vicariate" of his Spirit and of his apostles, and that it is the teaching Church which provides us infallibly with belief, inseparable from the faith of which it is the content.

What God has revealed. God has revealed all that it was

[1] 1 Cor. 4. 7; 15. 10.

necessary for us to know about him and about his plans for the world. He has done so throughout the history of Israel; he has perfected this revelation by Jesus Christ. The apostles, the hearers and witnesses of Christ, have handed on this revelation to the Church which has the mission of faithfully preserving and infallibly interpreting the revelation completed by Jesus Christ. The rule of our faith is thus the "tradition" of the Church, within which the Bible acts as a normative rule. The Word of God is within that living reality which is the Church; it is in the Church and by the Church that I hear the Word of God.[1]

· *Not because we have perceived its intrinsic truth by our reason.* It is impossible, for example, for us to perceive by our reason the presence of Jesus Christ in the Eucharist. We admit it because Christ has declared it to us and because the Church has infallibly transmitted to us these words of Christ and their proper interpretation.

It does not follow from these words of the Council that the mysteries which God has revealed to us are only "truths which we must believe although we cannot understand them". If they had no intelligible content, we might as well say that God addresses us in love, but "in double Dutch"! A mystery thus conceived would be an absurdity. If it cannot be "comprehended", it is in so far as it is unplumbable, inexhaustible. A mystery is not a wall against which you run your head, but an ocean into which you plunge. A mystery is not night; it is the sun, so brilliant that we cannot gaze at it, but so luminous that everything is illuminated by it. Jacques Rivière said: "Can you say that you do not understand that without which everything else is incomprehensible?"

Because of the authority of God. The Council's definition insists with extraordinary vigour upon the motive which justifies the assent of faith and gives it its special character in the order of knowledge. This capital point is a stumbling-block for most unbelievers, so we must dwell on it.

[1] See the books of this series on the subject.

Since there can be no question of demonstrating the Christian mysteries directly, or even of justifying them completely by their internal harmony or by the enlightenment which they afford, our belief in them can be founded only on the authority of God's witnesses. In regard to the truths of faith we are like a man who cannot prove for himself the existence of some distant country and must rely on a traveller who has been there and tells of what he saw:

"What we have heard, what we have seen with our own eyes, and our hands have handled . . . we announce to you" (1 John 1. 1).

But how can we be sure that these witnesses are reliable? When men bear witness to realities on their own level, within their own reach, it is relatively easy to find out whether or not they deserve our confidence. But when men claim to bear witness of God!

If we are to believe them God must guarantee them to us in some way. His own authority must, as it were, countersign the statements of these witnesses. And that is precisely what happens. There is in fact a double signing on God's part, one of an external kind, visible to the unbeliever and verifiable, apparently, by him, the other interior, invisible, perceptible only to the believer.

The first of these signings is *miracle*. We may recall the challenge thrown down by the prophet Elias to the prophets of Baal on Mount Carmel (1 Kings, 18. 20–40). Two holocausts are to be prepared; the prophets of Baal are to pray to their God; Elias will pray to Jahveh. The God who, without human intervention, sets fire to his holocaust is the true God.

Jesus himself appealed to his "works", that is, his miracles, as a motive of faith:

"If you are unwilling to believe because of me, believe because of the works that I perform" (John 5. 36; 10. 25; 10. 38).

Why is it that today not only does this argument from miracles seem to make no appeal to unbelievers but Christians themselves are ready to say: "I believe, not because of the miracles which the Christian tradition alleges, but in spite of them." This dislike of miracles is due partly to the spirit of critical inquiry, partly to religious feeling—partly to the former, because people fear that the supposedly miraculous is due to trickery or ignorance (so many natural phenomena were attributed to gods or demons which are explained today by science), partly to the latter, because faith and an encounter with the living God seem not to be in the same order as miracles.

This double dislike of miracles arises from a double misunderstanding. Short-sighted apologists have tried to make miracles a "rational" proof, by demonstrating that they are "contrary to the laws of nature". And so miracles have not been seen as God's word.

Our God is a God who speaks, and his speech (the Word) is all-powerful, effective: *Dixit et facta sunt*. That is why God speaks to us in deeds rather than in words (in the human sense of that term). God speaks to us by his creation, by the great events of Israel's history, by the "event which is Jesus Christ", and God's supreme Word was the resurrection of Jesus. These are the *mirabilia Dei* which have taught us that God is the author and the prince of life, that he is Love, that his promises and his gifts are freely given. . . .

The miracles may be called signs of God's purposes for the world, for they are all, in various ways, heralds of the resurrection of the flesh and of eternal life, the first streak of the dawn before that day on which souls and bodies together will be saved so as to live to God.

In this perspective, not only has miracle its function in summoning us to believe "on the authority of God", but also it becomes impossible to see how, apart from these *mirabilia Dei*, God's gracious plan could have been revealed to us. The events of the history of Israel or of the history of Jesus—and (let us repeat) the resurrection—are God's great words in which he has revealed himself to us and given us understanding of his designs. They are "deed-words".

This immediately suggests to us that a word requires to be heard. If it is true that a miracle is a sign wrought by God to attract our attention, its profound meaning cannot be understood except by one who sets himself to listen. The understanding of miracles presupposes a "religious" man, and we are brought back to what has been said earlier about the need for "opening" the soul if there is to be faith, but without in any way diminishing the importance of miracles. In this sense Pascal said: "An understanding of the promised time does not depend upon the heart. An understanding of promised goods does depend upon the heart, which calls 'good' that which it loves." In fine miracles are recognized only by those who are already on the move.

These reflections show us that the recognition of "God's authority" as the foundation of our faith cannot rest upon miracles alone, just as the understanding of revelation cannot be ascribed simply to the teaching of the apostles. We saw in the previous chapter that the Holy Spirit, the invisible preacher, gives the hearer the grace to adhere to the external word. In the same way we must conclude that God's great deeds in the history of salvation establish our faith in "God's authority" only through the Holy Spirit who bears witness in the depths of our hearts. St Paul has expressed this truth in a mysterious phrase:

"The Spirit himself thus assures our spirit that we are children of God" (Rom. 8. 16).

This, then, is the second "signing".

Certainly an analysis of the human consciousness does not enable us to discover this witness of the Spirit objectively. But when the Spirit dwells in a soul, he liberates and renews it. A man's whole inner life is changed, and he experiences a radical reorientation of his inner forces. Evil no longer overcomes him at every turn. He has an experience not of the Spirit himself, but of the effects and signs which reveal him. He no longer doubts that his faith is based on God's authority.

*   *   *

It is noteworthy that the Council of the Vatican, in its magisterial definition of faith, echoes what St Paul had already said so categorically:

"We give thanks to God unceasingly that, when we delivered the divine message to you, you recognized it for what it is, God's message, not man's; it is God, after all, who manifests his power in you that have learned to believe" (I Thess. 2. 13).

WE BELIEVE IN LOVE

At the close of this book we would sum up the essentials of our faith, as St John in old age condensed in his first epistle the results of his meditations and his religious experience, thereby bringing together all the themes of the Bible. We cannot do better than direct the reader to this document in which everything is said. But we might try to put into modern terms these words of John's:

"We have believed in Love".[1]

If we tried to declare our faith to unbelievers in a matter of minutes we should do so in roughly the following way: We believe there is an absolute eternal Being, existing of himself, from whom all other beings derive their existence. This Being we call God. We believe in him as a Person, because, being persons, "subjects", ourselves, we can think of God only as higher than ourselves, as a super-person.

We believe that God is Love, that Love makes him what he is, that the life of God is an interchange of absolute love between three persons. We believe that the Father is all Love, that he engenders a Son who is all his love, and that between the Father and the Son there is a living kiss of love, a breath of love, which we call "Spirit" because of the derivation of the Latin word *spiritus*. But *spiritus*, like *pneuma* in Greek and *ruah* in Hebrew, signifies, far more than our "spirit", the breath of life.

We believe that creation is a sort of outward expression of

[1] 1 John, 4. 16.

this love of the Persons of the Trinity for one another, that it is planned by God so that he may join to himself beings worthy of his love.

We find it quite in order that such a plan should imply freedom and the time-series; there can be no love except between free beings and, in our world, freedom cannot be effectively exercised except by gradual movements and so in a time-series. Thus we are not surprised to find that the world's history is a sort of groping movement upwards towards freedom. The history of life shows itself to us as a search for freedom on the part of beings which—through an increasing complexity of their organisms—are gradually freeing themselves from the shackles of their environment.

With man there appears on the earth a being who is really free and so capable of a relation of love with his Creator, a being "in the image and likeness of God". After a long pre-history which remains profoundly mysterious to us, after hundreds of thousands of years, God entered—so to speak—upon the stage of history when he revealed himself to Abraham, the father of all "believers".

From that time on, the "sacred history" of humanity is well known to us: it is a divine pedagogy of eighteen centuries during which God addresses Israel as his chosen people down to the day when—"the time being fulfilled"—the Son of God became man to contract the eternal alliance with mankind.

By this we mean that the Son of God has come to give us a share in his own divine sonship, to make us true children of the Heavenly Father, by incorporating us into himself. We become sons of God by sharing in the life of the only-begotten Son of the Father. By Jesus Christ, with him and in him, we enter into the Trinitarian life of God. The living kiss of love, the Spirit, who unites the Son with the Father, unites us also with the Father. In Jesus Christ, God has become man in order that man may become God.

Henceforth no event can be compared with this. In Jesus everything is given to us. He is the key to all history, the centre and the explanation of the entire universe. History indeed goes on, but it has no other meaning save the growth of Christ in the world, the completion of Christ's Body. When Christ is "total", this world will burst into the new earth and new heaven which will realize for ever the marriage of God with his creation.

*   *   *

A hymn of unsurpassable beauty expresses this unfolding of God's plan: the prologue of the Fourth Gospel. It has been arranged below in two columns so as to bring out the parallelism between the last verse and the first, the last but one with the second, and so forth. Read first down and then up:

THE PROLOGUE OF JOHN

1-2. At the beginning of time the Word already was; and God had the Word abiding with him, and the Word was God.

18. No man has ever seen God; but now his only-begotten Son, who abides in the bosom of the Father, has himself become our interpreter.

3. It was through him that all things came into being, and without him came nothing that has come to be.

17. Through Moses the law was given to us; Through Jesus Christ grace came to us, and truth.

4-5. In him there was life, and that life was the light of men. And the light shines in darkness, a darkness which was not able to master it.

16. We have all received something out of his abundance, grace answering to grace.

6–8. A man appeared, sent
from God, whose
name was John.
He came for a witness,
to bear witness of the
light,
so that through him all
men might learn to
believe.
He was not the Light;
he was sent to bear wit-
ness to the light.

15. We have John's witness to
him;
I told you, cried John,
there was one coming
after me who takes rank
before me;
He was when I was not.

9–11. There is one who en-
lightens every soul
born into the world;
he was the true Light.
He, through whom the
world was made, was
in the world,
and the world treated
him as a stranger.
He came to what was
his own, and they
who were his own
gave him no wel-
come.

14. And the Word was made
flesh,
and came to dwell among
us;
and we had sight of his
glory,
glory such as belongs to
the Father's only-
begotten Son,
full of grace and truth.

12–13. But all those who did welcome him he empowered to become the children of God, all those who believe in his
name; their births came, not from human stock, not
from nature's will or man's, but from God.

A whole book would be needed for a commentary on this;
I can only indicate the movement of thought.

The first verses (1–2) tell us of the Word of God, existing
before anything began. It is with God. It is God. Then (3) we
see that the Word is the author of Creation, and that everything
subsists in him, the second part of the verse expressing this
second idea (cf. Col. 1. 16). In verses 4–5 the last word of one
line becomes the first word of the next, and these "linking"

words: "life", "light" and "darkness", keep on evoking the first page of Genesis so as to suggest to us that Jesus is the author of a new Creation. The work of Jesus will be described, in John's Gospel, as a parallel with the work of creation on the first page of the Bible.

Verses 6–8 (like their parallel, verse 15) are more prosaic and break the rhythm of the poem. They are probably additions. But they are in place as part of the movement of thought, showing as they do how God's revelation pursues its course. After creating everything and making everything subsist in his life and his light, the Word has spoken by the prophets who are summed up in the person of John the Baptist.

But the Word himself is the light who never ceases to come into the world. He is eternally "he-who-is-coming" (9–10). (Cf. Apoc. 22. 17, 20.)

In particular he has come to his own, the Jews, and they have not received him (11). God always asks hospitality from men so that they may have hospitality in him. And we have the terrible power of keeping the door shut against him. (Apoc. 3. 20.)

But to those who received him (by faith, first of all), the Word gives the power to become what he is himself: God's son, life and light. "God was made man that man might be made God", the Fathers of the Church made bold to say. Jesus Christ, whom God engendered both in his eternal birth in the Father's heart and in his temporal birth in the Virgin's womb, communicates to us his own divine sonship. Thus John has silently inserted Mary into the middle of his prologue.

Henceforth, he whom John has called so far the Word, and whom he will now begin to call "the only-begotten Son", is to realize, on a properly divine level, all that Genesis and Exodus had shown us on the earthly level. The Word has become "flesh", taking on humanity with its weaknesses. He plants among us definitively that tent in which, during the Exodus, he was considered to dwell (the word translated by "dwell" in the text means precisely "planted his tent"). The glory of God which filled the tent during the Exodus and was the manifestation of the divine presence has been seen in the miracles, the transfiguration and the resurrection of Jesus. This glory has assured us of the two guarantees of the Alliance (according to Exodus): the merciful love of God and his fidelity (*emeth*, from a root which means: firm, solid. Cf. *amen*). The Incarnation realizes in truth and in fullness the Alliance which was only foreshadowed by the Alliance contracted with Moses.

John the Baptist bore witness to Christ's pre-existence, that is, the pre-existence of him who *is* from all eternity (15) (cf. John 8. 58).

He in whom dwells the fullness of the divinity in corporeal form has come to communicate this divine life to us (16). Jesus has realized in truth and in fullness (17) what the book of Exodus has told us (it acts as a sort of background to the fourth Gospel). Not only is he himself the grace and the fullness of God (14), but he has communicated those qualities to the hearts of men (as Ezech. 36. 26 prophesied).

Verse 18 is a condensation of the whole poem. We are summoned to see face to face (1 John 3. 2) God who is the Unknowable, whom no man has seen at any time, whom no one can see and live (Exodus 33. 20: Isaias 6. 5), because the Father's well-beloved Son, he who lives in such intimate union with the Father, has wished to raise the veil which concealed him (Luke 16. 22), and to lead us to the Father.

Such is the synthesis of our faith. The unknowable God, whose life is an interchange of love between three infinite Persons, has wished to create in order to unite to himself beings worthy of his love. He has created by his Son and in his Son. Creation is the work of the Word who animates it and unceasingly tries—if we may so put it—to make himself present in the human consciousness and to find hospitality there. Jesus Christ is the supreme "epiphany" of God and his dwelling among us, so as to communicate to us the divine sonship and to introduce us, poor creatures that we are, into this intimacy with the Father which is the joy of the Trinitarian life.

After joyfully contemplating the synthesis of our whole faith in this passage of St John's we must remember that we can believe in Love only by loving. This does not mean simply that the love of God for us requires that we should love God and love our brethren; that is obvious (whatever our short-comings in fulfilling this obligation!). *Caritas Dei urget nos.*

But I want to repeat in conclusion that *believing means loving,* that is, it is indispensable to love in order to believe. Let us consult human experience. Do you suppose that this young man would betroth himself to this young woman unless he loved her? The very word "betroth" implies confidence and faith. The faith of the young man in her whom he loves is present, too, long before the day of the betrothal. His confidence was born along with his knowledge of the girl, and this knowledge itself was only possible through an interest in her which had been already aroused by love and in love. The Bible has an astonishing word to express conjugal love: "Abraham *knew* Sara".

So to gain faith and to increase it we cannot do better than to open our hearts to love, to the love of our brethren, the pledge and condition of our love of God, but also to the love of God himself—"But how can I love before I believe?" Life laughs at our logic. Readiness to love is love already. The thirst for love is love already. Have an "open" soul.

And also do not separate the love of God from the love of our brethren. The more you read the Gospel the more you will be persuaded that we must love the world and God with one and the same love, and that we must love them both *for themselves.*

The love of God enables us to distinguish what is living from what is dead in the world, what bears fruit and what does not, what can be taken over by Christ and what is unserviceable.

Love of the world prevents us from reducing the love of God to a possessive love: "God and myself". Love of the world makes us love the total Christ who is still growing to completion, makes us work with him as much as live by him. The

Lord requires of us first of all that each should become a "we". To the extent to which each is absorbed into this "we", which is his living Body, Christ transforms us into himself. So far are human relationships, thus conceived, from being in opposition to solitude with God that they drive us to God. They arouse temptations, conflicts, problems. . . . We feel ourselves appallingly free and responsible, and our human relationships can find their equilibrium only in God.

Let us end by joining together these two statements:

"It is by faith that we are saved" (St Paul).

"At the close of our lives it is by Love that we shall be judged" (St John of the Cross).

SELECT BIBLIOGRAPHY

COVENTRY, John, S.J.: *Faith seeks Understanding: an Essay on Faith and Reason*, London and New York, Sheed & Ward, 1951.

DANIELOU, Jean, S.J.: *God and Us*, London, Mowbray, 1957.

DANIELOU, Jean, S.J.: *God and the Ways of Knowing*, New York, Meridian Books.

D'ARCY, M. C., S.J.: *Belief and Reason*, London, Burns & Oates, 1944; Springfield, Illinois, Templegate, 1947.

D'ARCY, M. C., S.J.: *The Nature of Belief*, London and New York, Sheed & Ward, 1951.

DE LUBAC, H., S.J.: *The Drama of Atheistic Humanism*, London and New York, Sheed & Ward, 1953.

GUARDINI, Romano: *Faith and Modern Man*, London, Burns & Oates, 1953; New York, Pantheon, 1952.

MCNABB, Vincent, O.P.: *Faith and Prayer*, London, Blackfriars, 1953; Westminster, Maryland, Newman, 1954.

TRETHOWAN, Dom Illtyd: *Certainty*, London, Dacre Press, 1948.

CARMELITE MONASTERY
Dudley Hill